KU-350-441

£3

HITLER WAS A
VEGETARIAN

Hitler was a Vegetarian

and other tales

RON FERGUSON

Northern Books
from Famedram

From the same author:

Donald Dewar ate my Hamster

Black Diamonds and the Blue Brazil

Geoff: the Life of Geoffrey M Shaw

ISBN 0905489 713
© *Copyright 2001 Ron Ferguson and* The Herald

Published by Famedram Publishers Ltd AB41 9EA
www.northernbooks.co.uk

Printed by Thomson Press Ltd
C35 Phase II Noida India

Contents

Foreword

by Mark Douglas-Home, editor of *The Herald*

I have come to realise that there are only three types of newspaper columnist. There is the 'expert' who impresses you with an encyclopaedic knowledge of, and opinions about, world crises and matters of state.

Then there is the 'confidant' who builds a relationship with you by intimate disclosure – romance, diet, work, babies, health – quite like Bridget Jones and her diary.

Finally, there is the 'conversationalist' who, from nowhere, suddenly becomes your best friend, even though you have never met. He or she engages you with a mixture of entertaining personal anecdote and experience intermingled with wisdom and knowledge.

It is an odd best friendship because you don't say a word, but somehow this once-a-week, one-way conversation becomes part of your life. Every time you read the column two things happen: you enjoy it, and you learn something important about the world about you.

Ron Ferguson is a columnist like this. You are overtaken by this conviction that if you ever met him you could talk to him, that you could pick up the conversation just where he left off the week before.

Recently, a reader sent me a letter. "Thank you," it began, "for Ron Ferguson. I don't know what I would do without him." This is the skill, and the influence, of the best columnists: to become indispensable to complete strangers. By the time that you have finished reading this book, I am sure that you too will have acquired a new best friend.

Introduction

The reception accorded *Donald Dewar ate my Hamster,* a collection of my columns from *The Herald,* has emboldened Famedram's Bill Williams, two years on, to produce this new book of columns and short stories.

I am grateful to Mark Douglas-Home, editor of *The Herald,* not only for readily granting permission to reproduce the columns, but for writing the foreword to this book. Mark and executive editor Colin McDiarmid have been a great source of encouragement to me. I am also grateful to *The Herald* for permission to reproduce four of the short stories in the book, *Hitler was a Vegetarian, Scotland, Scotland, A day in the death of a minister,* and *The Christmas Illumination of Sir Geeza Bung.*

My thanks are also due to Bill McArthur, cartoonist with *The Herald* and the *Financial Times,* for his illustrations. Bill is a class act.

Above all, my thanks are due to the readers of *The Herald,* with whom I am privileged to have a weekly conversation. My postbag tells me that readers do not always agree with me, but the responses challenge, inspire and often entertain.

I would like also to express thanks to the congregation of St Magnus Cathedral, Kirkwall, with whom I've also been privileged to have a weekly conversation, in this case for 11 years. Having now embarked on a full-time writing adventure, still based in Orkney, I appreciate and value so many supportive friendships forged in times of sadness and celebration.

RON FERGUSON
Kirkwall

11

The Columns

It's Bleedin' Obvious Mate

Night and day, this column has been toiling tirelessly in the vineyards of human knowledge. My researchers have been out interviewing people at work, in their homes, in the streets. (Though I do like Evelyn Waugh's contention that the "man in the street" does not exist. "There are individual men and women, each one of whom has an individual and immortal soul, and such beings need to use streets from time to time.") Who funds these research projects of mine? Universities, Women's Rural Institutes, the Vatican, The World Bank, Alastair Campbell, and the Hunchback of Notre Dame. Who pays, wins.

This column, for instance, was commissioned by the Queen's University of Bonkle to investigate the ways in which male and female dogs urinate. After close observation and random interviews, and after setting up a control group of mixed canines with their legs tied together, my researchers concluded that lady dogs sort of sit down, while gentlemen dogs lift one of their legs. Why do the males do this? One labrador told my interviewer:

"It's bleedin' obvious, mate. It's preferable to urinating on your leg. And we only lift one leg, because if you try to lift two, you end up on the grass. That's rhyming slang, mate, by the way."

15

More sensational results came from a study commissioned by the Loyal Orange Order of Morningside. They asked us to set up a series of tests to see how Rangers and Celtic supporters responded to colours. We stopped people in the street, and asked them what school they went to. We then held up colour charts. Our research established conclusively that Rangers supporters tend to gravitate towards the colour blue, while Celtic supporters are more "green minded". Might we suggest, on the basis of these conclusions, that the Rangers board of directors should design a blue strip for their players, and that Celtic should play in green?

We were commissioned by the University of Lochgelly (a former chip shop) to produce a report on the differences between men and women. After a series of 'blind' tests and gropes, our researches came up with conclusions that are equally astounding. Here is the definitive, unchallengeable conclusion: 91 % of women have sort of growths upon their chests, whereas 89 % of men have bits hanging precariously from their bodies. It all goes to show, does it not?

Here are some more amazing results. On one of our famous comprehensive surveys, 93% of women admitted to sometimes lying about their age. (The other 7% were lying.) Drinking lots of beer gives men what are sometimes referred to as "beer bellies". Children quite often prefer holidays to school. People in the police and the armed forces tend to wear uniforms when they are on duty. And did you know that when men and women are happy, the corners of their mouths have a tendency to turn upwards?

Now, it's confession time: this column hasn't actually conducted any of these surveys. (If you thought any of it was true, you're in worse shape than you thought you were.) What prompted these delirious musings was an article in the *New Scientist* pointing out that a lot of costly

16

modern research merely establishes what our grannies telt us for free. For instance, the magazine reveals that the University of Pittsburgh monitored the body fat and cholesterol of 535 women to see how they could avoid putting on weight, and came to the astonishing conclusion that they should exercise and have a low-fat diet.

A study set up by the University of South Carolina apparently showed that people were less likely to yell at their boss than at their family, because their boss had the power to fire them. Well I never! An expensive study by Iowa State University revealed that "children take after their parents". Wow! It also found that children were more likely to smoke if their parents did because of "gender symmetry" - which our grannies used to call "like father, like son". Nowadays, our grannies could charge huge consultancy fees.

Did you know, by the way, that a journal called *Proceedings of the National Academy of Sciences* has revealed exclusively that freezing temperatures were responsible for the death of Captain Scott and his men in 1912? And here was me thinking that the whole gang had choked on Smarties in their wee tent.

Writing about the phenomenon of researching the already known, *New Scientist* says: "Brits call it the Bleedin' Obvious, for Americans it's the No-Brainer. It comes about when researchers shy away from the trackless jungle at the edge of knowledge and set up camp on more familiar territory." So much money, so little commonsense.

And did you know that the editor commissioned this column to do an exhaustive analysis of the *Herald's* readership? Our dramatic and expensive conclusion? 83% are Scots who can read. Editor, your cheque (to me) is in the post.

Great Scottish moral theatre with no turn left unstoned

Society has gone downhill. Some people place the beginning of the decline in the permissive Sixties, others root the trouble in the Industrial Revolution. Some historians go even further back - they trace the moral declension to the years of the Enlightenment, when reason was enthroned in place of religion. But that's much too recent: the rot set in centuries ago when people were allowed to get off with things too easily, and didn't have to face proper punishments.

It all began when society stopped stoning transgressors. Take homosexuals. The Book of Leviticus clearly states that if a man lies with a man, both of them should be put to death. Why don't we reintroduce that penalty? That would soon sort the buggers out! The same book also states unequivocally: "Nor shall there come upon you a garment of cloth made of two kinds of material." I can exclusively reveal that this is why Marks & Spencers are going down the tubes. People who wear shirts of mixed materials should be hunted down forthwith. Here's another command from the book of Leviticus: "Everyone who curses his father or his mother shall surely be put to death." The message is unambiguous, and those who try to get away from the obvious meaning of the text should themselves be stoned. In fact, stoning is too good for 'em.

The book of Deuteronomy is equally firm. If a man has a stubborn or rebellious son who refuses to obey his parents, the youth is to be taken out to the gate of the city and denounced before the elders, "then all the men of the city shall stone him to death." Quite right. Here's more. If a bridegroom believes that the wedding night evidence shows that his bride was not a virgin, "then they shall bring out the young woman to the door of her father's house, and the men of the city shall stone her to death." Time we brought back these stable family values, and stopped the trendies destroying our society! And when we are not busy stoning, we can do a bit of holy hand-chopping.

Deuteronomy states that if there is a fight between two men, and the wife of one approaches his opponent and "puts out her hand and seizes him by the private parts, then you shall cut off her hand; your eye shall have no pity."

No pity! Stone the queers! Zap the rebellious teenagers! Kill the non-virgin brides! Destroy those who curse their parents! Cut off the squeezing hand! Punish those who do pick-and-mix with these commandments! Denounce those theologians who provide spurious reasons for setting aside the literal meaning of the texts! Get back to basics!

Today, this column proudly launches Scotland's first "Bring Back Stoning" campaign. I will hold a press conference, at which I will reveal the names of some prominent backers. I already have some names on faxes, so I can guarantee there will be big surprises (*especially for the people you name - ed.*) I am so confident that I have the public on my side that I am prepared to launch a Scotland-wide referendum on the subject. This will be preceded by a national debate on stoning. I will send totally unbiased literature to every abode in Scotland, no matter how humble. I will enclose catalogues with pictures of different sizes of stones. I can count on my friends in the tabloids to report the pros and cons of stoning dispassionately and compassionately, with headings like STONE THE CROWS! and GOTCHA GAYS!

I want the first stone-throwers to be people with clean hands, so I am planning to invite two holy monks whose saintly virtues have already been extolled in this column - Brother Irvine, the shy, retiring former editor of the "family-values" Scottish *Sun*, and the eirenic, soft-spoken Brother Clarke, editor-in-chief of the *Daily Record*.

These godly men have experience of targeting sinners. Both are free from prejudice; indeed, some of their best friends have been stoned. They also know about loonies, such as the barmy MSPs who are bent (on destroying our Christian culture). I will offer the tv stoning rights to BSkyB (sports channel), whose sainted owner, Brother Murdoch, is an exemplar of unworldliness. A cleric in a frock (not made of mixed material) will preach an admonitory homily while assuring the malefactors, with tears in his eyes, that he hates the sin but loves the sinner.

In this great Scottish moral theatre, no turn will be left unstoned. I will also invite dear Brother Robertson, our Bank of Scotland sponsored-American evangelist friend, to sing "The Dark Island". And as the bricks are reverently passed around, the Pure Gospel Male Voice Lumberjack Choir will sing their lovely hit song, "Stone a poof for Jesus!" from their latest cd, *Levitical Rocks*. We must get back to the Stone Age before it's too late.

How the fur flies when you visit the flock

All things bright and beautiful,
All creatures great and small,
All things wise and wonderful -
The Lord God made them all.

So it's dogs 5, politicians 0. During the by-election campaign at Anniesland, three SNP canvassers were bitten, one Labour activist was chewed by a West Highland terrier when he stuck his hand in a letter box, and a LibDem, Dr Tamsin Maybery (a very LibDemish sort of name), was bitten on the elbow by a low-class mongrel. The Tories got no bites: but they didn't get too many votes, either.

I don't suppose the public is grief-stricken at the biting of the soundbiters. This column has some fellow-feeling, though, for politicians with teeth-marks in their rear ends because I've been there, done that, got the injections. How did it all come about?

Well, there I was, doing the Lord's work in Easterhouse, when one of the Lord's creatures - an alsatian which answered, or more correctly didn't answer, to "Prince" - decided to attach itself, by its teeth, to my ecclesiastical erse (as uncouth Irish people would call it.)

Was I delighted, at that precise moment, to be communing so closely with the animal kingdom? Was I, like the great St Francis Assisi, full of benevolent thoughts about God's creatures? No I was not. I was, truth to tell, trying to kick this particular heavenly creature in the sphericals, as the lower classes refer to these appendages.

Now, it is extraordinarily difficult to kick a wolf which has a vice-like grip on your posterior. Try it for yourself. If you're at home, order your dug to sink its teeth into your backside (as people in Bearsden call it after a few sherries) and see how hard it is to kick a whirling beast. If you don't have a dog, stand up now and try it notionally. As you will find out, even an imaginary dog attached to your posterior is hard to kick, for the simple reason that it is always, as it were, behind you. (If you're unfortunate enough to be in a ScotRail compartment at the moment, your performance will astound and entertain the weary passengers as they sit, morose and languid, in a siding at Croy.)

Anyway, the Easterhouse anti-clerical alsatian with lockjaw was eventually persuaded by its owner to come in for its dinner. He shouted to me - the man that is, not the alsatian - "Sorry, pal." It was somehow reassuring, even touching, to be called "pal" at that particular moment. You must always look on the bright side of life.

Visiting the flock can expose the unsuspecting minister or priest to all sorts of hazards. I once visited a manic bird-lover who insisted on opening his budgie's cage while our conversation progressed. Now my idea of a superb evening does not include sitting in an enclosed space with a swirling bird. In no time, the budgie took on the aspect of a gigantic, threatening, Hitchcockian hawk. It sat on the mantelpiece looking malevolently in my direction, then it suddenly made for my head like a feathered cruise missile. At the last minute, it applied its brakes and landed gently on the bridge of my spectacles. Let me tell you, from experience, that it is exceedingly difficult to sustain a serious conversation about the nature of the Holy Trinity with a budgie perambulating back and forward on your specs.

Dogs can be a particular problem for clerics, because kicking the more hostile ones can lose you members of your congregation – whole dynasties, in the case of rural parishes. Even a quick, surreptitious prod at small but perfectly formed canine testicles, while people are apparently absorbed in your fascinating discourse on the subject of the Apostolic Succession, will be observed and reported to the next kirk session. This is what it means to be dog-collared.

No, when the apocalyptic Hound of the Baskervilles hurtles towards you and leaps on to your lap as you sit sedately eating scones and drinking tea, you must remain calm and Christian. "Don't worry, Jasper won't touch you," the lady of the house will insist. (That's what the Romans said to the Christians when they released the lions.) Soon Jasper will have his paws round your neck and will be licking your face with a tongue that has explored things which cannot be mentioned in a family column.

Let me tell you about an even trickier problem. Some dogs have an insatiable desire to stick their long snouts into men's crotches. Why this should be, in the great scheme of things, I have no idea. All I know is that the canine snitch has an unerring homing instinct, one which can transform a kindly pastoral visit into a piece of grotesque ecclesiastical theatre. "He must be smelling your dog!" cries the lady of the house. Eh? Even as you back away, bent double, Prince's uncannily invasive snout manages to root around the territory. Is this why bishops carry crooks? There is nothing in the scriptures about how to deal with this situation.

There's worse. Sometimes a Jack Russell will attempt -

how can I put this delicately? – sexual congress with your leg. The louder the embarrassed hostess trills, "Leave the minister alone, Horace!" the more Humping Horace will engage in unPresbyterian conduct. The frenzied, unseemly activity going on down below indubitably detracts from your lofty observations about the sexual obsessions of modern society. This is definitely not the time to kneel for prayer.

All things wise and wonderful, the Lord God made them all. As the west of Scotland's metaphysically untutored would put it: Why, but?

Only a stone's throw from everywhere

I've been stoned for the last few weeks. So while I'm still in an altered state of consciousness, I want to talk to you about sin.

Ready for a bit of that old-time religion? Good. Here goes. The Bible is against sin. Okay so far? Near the top of the premier league of sins is usury - the taking of interest on a loan. The Christian Church maintained the ban right up until the late Middle Ages, when the rise and rise of dynamic capitalism saw the quiet jettisoning of the prohibition on usury. By comparison, references to homosexuality in the Bible are few and far between - Third Division stuff. Jesus never mentions the subject, though he does have a great deal to say about money and exploitation. His chucking of the moneylenders out of the temple was a conscious piece of religious theatre.

Recently, I wrote a satirical piece calling for the reintroduction of stoning. Soon, real bricks were flying. I discovered that Orkney is only a stone's throw from everywhere. The poor Kirkwall postie groaned under the weight of spiritual death threats and sundry cheery Christian greetings.

The trouble with parody is that real life turns out to be

even more absurd than anything a mere columnist can send up. For instance, I am grateful to the religious historian, Karen Armstrong, for timely information about the Reconstructionist Movement. Their vision of a future godly society, apparently, is one in which slavery will be reintroduced, birth control banned, and homosexuals, blasphemers, and disobedient children stoned to death. O Happy Day!

The Reconstructionists are seriously loopy, but they are at least consistent. They insist that if you are going to take the Bible literally, you must (a) apply every rule and (b) enforce every punishment. They accuse conservative evangelicals of essentially being pic'n'mix liberals.

In all the messages from angry Christians, I have never yet received a straight answer to this straight question: what are the grounds for being literalist about gays, but non-literalist over non-virgin brides, rebellious sons, and usurers? I detect a great deal of anger directed at gays, but not at capitalists. Why? Here is a great irony: Brian Souter, bankroller of the "Keep the Clause" campaign, is a Christian fundamentalist, yet his great wealth has been achieved by a highly competitive and at times predatory use of the power of money - which, according to the Bible, is strictly forbidden. Am I missing something here?

Now questions about sexuality are notoriously complex. They cannot be resolved theologically by wrenching texts from their contexts and using them like weapons, any more than prohibitions designed to protect vulnerable people in a primitive agrarian economy can be applied straightforwardly to 21st century banking. Any joined-up moral theology has to search out underlying principles, and reflect on them in the contemporary context. Selective appeals to biblical literalism are simply not on.

Here is another paradox. The Keep the Clause

campaign insists that it is not motivated by prejudice against gays. Why, then, has it chosen a noted foul-mouthed homophobe to be its public spokesman? Mr Irvine's tabloid column is enlightening. How about such charming words as "slobbering queers who want to get their hands on young boys' arses"? Fact: the vast majority of paedophiles are heterosexuals. If we are serious about protecting our children, should we not have a campaign against the "promotion" of heterosexuality?

Now think about the following personages: Socrates, Alexander the Great, Michelangelo, Leonardo da Vinci, Tchaikovsky, Marcel Proust, Sir Benjamin Britten, Gertude Stein, Virginia Wolf, and Rabbi Lionel Blue. If a teacher tells the truth about these randomly chosen gays and lesbians, is he or she open to a charge of "promoting" homosexuality under the terms of Section 28? Yes. (After all, we can't expect a poofter like Michelangelo, painter of the Sistine Chapel frescoes, to be as good a role model as Jack Irvine, former editor of the Scottish *Sun*, can we?) As a parent, I sympathise with parents' genuine concerns; but whatever the question is, Brian Souter and Jack Irvine are not the answer.

All that this hysterical debate and shambolic, seriously flawed opinion poll - the pointless outcome of which Mr Irvine is duty bound to claim as a victory - have done is to escalate hatred and abuse against an already monsterised minority whose troublesome, unasked-for inheritance already brings them social grief. They could be the son or daughter or grandchild of any of us. As with the heterosexual majority, there are serious concerns about promiscuity (and "Outrage", the obnoxious gay militant tendency is as unlovable as it gets); but most gays - like the rest of us - want loving and committed relationships and a bit of human happiness.

Some of the messages coming from churches to gays

are truly abysmal. Where is our compassion, for Christ's sake?

Sadly, the dealers in hard emotional currency have taken over the temple. Protestant and Catholic, they move seamlessly, in spotless robes, from highly combustible "Christian" sexual rhetoric to the matter of church pension investments - without a word, not a single word, about usury. After all, it wouldn't do to go back to the Bible, would it?

Minister and the hound from hell

Ah, the trials of the clergy! The piece I wrote recently about ministers being savaged by parishioners' family pets produced an astonishing response. Sobbing clergypersons of all genders or none confided to me tales of being pinioned by dogs, circumcised by cats, chased by geese, butted by goats and battered by budgies – all while innocently going about the Lord's business. Some of the stories are too outrageous to be printed in this family column. Others had me crying with laughter, which is not the most sympathetic response when a brother minister is describing the teethmarks in his clerical posterior.

I must tell you – confidentially of course – about one minister, whose name I will not give to the tabloids (not for less than ten grand, anyway). When he approached the local "big hoose" to pay a pastoral visit, a dog came bounding up to him, snarling and threatening. As the hound from hell drew nearer, an upstairs window opened, and the lady of the manor instructed the clergyman in stentorian tones, "Kick the dog's balls!"

Surprised by the directness of the command, but knowing that the gentry are often uninhibited in such matters, the meenister duly obliged, with relish. The dug was last seen disappearing over the horizon, howling with pain. Just as the door of the big hoose opened, the minister turned a whiter shade of pale when he noticed that on the lawn were two coloured balls, the kicking of which was a sure-fire way of distracting a much-loved, boisterous family pet. Oh dear, oh dear, oh dear.

Even without the beasts, pastoral visits are full of pitfalls, some of which can lead to a parting of the ecclesiastical ways. The refusal of tea and scones can be interpreted as a serious insult. Some scones represent a comprehensive assault on the human digestive system. I know of one cleric who accepted the offer of a cup of tea, which tasted like poison. When the lady went through to the kitchen, he checked if there were any pot plants which might absorb the lethal brew, then noticed that the window was open. He quickly moved over and threw the tea out. The next sound he heard was the smashing of china on the pavement below, while the handle of the cup dangled on his finger. Ach well.

Ric Holland, former Methodist minister in the Milton area of Glasgow and a former director of the Glasgow Volunteer Bureau, told me of a wee embarrassment he had when he was a young student for the ministry. As part of their training, ordinands were sent out to preach on the Methodist circuit. On one occasion, he was boarded with a local widow.

When he was shown to his room, he realised that the woman's bedroom was between his room and the bathroom. Now, he didn't normally need to get up in the middle of the night, but once the notion was in his head, it worked its way downwards towards his bladder. He woke at 2am, and, being at that time a shy and retiring lad, he was determined not to go through the widow's bedroom in order to get to the loo. Instead he prayed that the problem would go away. By three in the morning he was beside himself. What to do? Ah, the window. He prised it open, silently. Relief at last. How was he to know that below the bedroom window was a shed with a tin roof? It could have been worse, though. The fraying sash rope might have snapped, and the lady might have had to rescue him. Don't even think about it.

Anyway, as you enjoy your winter festivities spare a kindly thought for your friendly neighbourhood minister or priest - out in all weathers, heroically facing Alsatians, lions, wildcats, geese, goats, hawks, parrots, and scones like bullets. And when, after yet another mission impossible, I examine my scars and swallow my Rennies, I will raise a glass to you, gentle reader.

A radical cure for headaches

There you have it. The best winter beer in the UK is brewed in Orkney and is called *Skullsplitter*. Judges at the Campaign for Real Ale's national winter celebration of beer in Manchester decided that the fruity, 8.5% barley wine should be named Supreme Champion Winter Beer of Britain 2001.

At the announcement, the Campaign's Scottish director, Colin Valentine, said the accolade proved that Orkney Brewery could produce beers to perform on the national stage with companies 100 times their size. He said: "This is tremendous news for Orkney Brewery and a shot in the arm for Scottish brewing. It's the first time a Scottish brewer has taken the gold medal, and it's a just reward for Orkney's commitment to brewing original and distinctive beers." Orkney Brewery also won the silver prize in the Strong Mild and Old Ale category of the competition with their *Dark Island* beer.

Skullsplitter is quite a beer. But the man after whom the beer is named was quite a guy. Earl Thorfinn, first Viking ruler of all Orkney, did not get his nickname because he was a gentle fellow. If you were an innocent wee Pict going about your lawful business in Kirkwall in the ninth century, you would cross the road in order to avoid meeting Thorfinn the Skullsplitter. If you got on the wrong side of him, he would offer you a radical cure for your headache. He would chop off your heid. None of this "I'm OK, you're OK" nonsense for Mr Skullsplitter.

Another man worth avoiding was Eirik Bloodaxe. His nickname told you everything you needed to know. He was another who didn't believe in win-win negotiations. It was always win-lose, with you losing. Eirik's daughter, Ragnhild, was even worse. She married the son of Earl Thorfinn. Yes, Thorfinn the Skullsplitter. So the Blood-axes married into the Skullsplitter family. It wasn't exactly a pacifist dynasty. ("Who have we got coming for dinner tonight, dear? Oh, the Blood-Axes. That'll be nice.")

Ragnhild murdered three husbands before they twigged that something funny was going on. Those who think that the world would be a more peaceable place if women were in charge should read the *Orkneyinga Saga* to cure themselves of that illusion. Frakokk, wife of Ljot the Renegade, made a poisoned shirt in order to kill her sister Helga's son, as part of another game of happy royal families. ("Try this on, dear. It'll fit you like a glove.") Unfortunately, another punter put it on by mistake and went straight to the happy hunting ground.

These were cheery Viking days. In order to pass the dark winter days, people played a primitive game of rugby, using a severed Scottish head as a ball. This is believed (by the Orkney Tourist Board) to be the origin of the Ba' Game between the Uppies and the Doonies which is played even now in the streets of Kirkwall on Christmas and New Year's Day.

What insipid times we live in nowadays! We cure headaches by means of aspirin. How boring! We have spin-doctors leaking quiet malice instead of doing the honest thing by sticking a poisoned shirt on an enemy. And nowadays, our names tell people nothing. Tony Blair. William Hague. Not like Magnus Bare-legs, Einar Belly-

Shaker, Arni-Pinleg, Botof the Stubborn, Halfdan Longleg, Olaf Tit-bit, Sigurd the Fake-Deacon and all the other crazed characters who limp or slaughter their way through the Orkney sagas.

These were the days when men were men, and women were shirt-makers to royalty. Life wasn't boring – it was just short. Just when you thought you'd got life in Kirkwall sussed, Thorfinn the Skullsplitter crossed the road in order to have the kind of rapid conversation that did your heid in.

Aye, people had more fun in the old days. They might have been poor, but they were never bored. Not when guys like Eirik Blood-Axe were treading the earth. These were men you could look up to. There was more discipline, as well, when Thorfinn and Eirik were free to give you a clip around the lug, or even chop your lug off. No interfering social workers then! There was also more respect for authority and royalty. You would always call a man like Stary-Eyed the Horrible "sir". (Okay, I just made that name up, but you get my drift.)

That kind of society also saved a fortune by not having law courts and soft stuff like that. Thorfinn or Eirik simply decapitated the troublemakers. That taught the cheeky sods a lesson! Nor did Kirkwall have the expense of looking after the elderly. The cut-off point was about thirty. No nonsense about Sutherland reports then!

Ah, the good old days. I'm going to have a pint of *Skullsplitter*, and dream. Good beer, this. Blows your bleeding head off.

Advice for Sodus Luckius

Dear Wills, (Please forgive my familiarity, but we St Andreans must stick together.) I was delighted that, out of all the British universities you might have chosen, you went for my alma mater. It is a choice, I'm sure, that you won't regret.

It is not the prerogative of columnists to advise royalty. Indeed, it would be cheeky and presumptuous to do so. But columnists are cheeky and presumptuous, and even get paid the odd "bawbee" (a quaint Scottish term for the Euro) for their labours on behalf of a grateful nation. So I'm going to do it anyway.

But how did I, a man of humble origins, get through the great portals of St Andrews University? The story begins with an ancient parchment found high on a hill by a lonely goatsherd in Tibet. Its hieroglyphics revealed that the next Holy Llama would be found in Cowdenbeath. The wise men from the East hunted excitedly through the coal bings of West Fife, and lo, under a heap of coal, they found a small but perfectly-formed being. Me. Yes, the prophesied Holy One of Cowdenbeath. They immediately put me down for Gordonstoun, where I drank copious amounts of cherry brandy, and knackered myself by flogging first year students and running up and down hills wearing a top hat. When it came to University, my advisers looked around for a place which would be secure against attack by supporters of rival Llamas based in Chinese restaurants, and which had a decent golf course. So St Andrews it was.

(Actually, sir, I must come clean: none of the above is true, even though, as the narrative moved on seamlessly, I was beginning to believe it myself. I wrote it to illustrate the fact that graduates of St Andrews University tend to be merry japesters. You will be one too, and your loyal subjects will be pleased. The truth is more prosaic: I was working happily in the fleshpots of journalism in Edinburgh until a gnarled and wizened 275-year-old leader of the ancient Kirk woke up with a start in the middle of the night and....)

Enough of this. What can Your Holiness expect when he goes to Fife? You will be a "bejant", a first year student in need of guidance and protection. You will choose a "senior man" and a "senior woman", who will teach you about Life. Choose with care. (Have you seen the film, *The Graduate*? Or the play of the same name, running in London at the moment, starring Jerry Hall? Do you get my drift, sir? If you don't, may I suggest respectfully that you are too young to go to St Andrews?)

As a bejant, you will wear your traditional red gown in the conventional manner. In second year, you will wear it off the right shoulder. In third year, off the left shoulder. In fourth year, you will wear it off both shoulders, and you will know what it feels like to be a model wearing a dress held together only by the Fourth Law of Thermo-dynamics.

You will probably be invited to join the Kate Kennedy Club. This will involve much "bevvying" (a quaint Scottish term for polite social drinking.) On Raisin Monday - an occasion of great frivolity - you will take part in a street pageant led by a personage on a white horse. (If you have been indulging in too much of the said "bevvying", you may follow the wrong white horse and find yourself

36

dressed as a fairy in the middle of a group of tense and serious-looking men wearing bowler hats and orange sashes. This is a mistake you will not make again.) If Your Highness is particularly popular, you may be chosen to play the part of Kate herself. In this case, you will wear a pretty dress and lots of make-up. This will be good training for life as a royal.

Students normally spend their first year in student residences, unwholesome places of disrepute characterised by "thrashes" - wild social occasions at which much Irn Bru is taken. I stayed in a small house of anarchy called Hepburn Hall. It had a mascot called "the beast" - a hairy, moth-eaten, diseased head of a buffalo or something, which was taken out and paraded on occasions of great historical insignificance. Just the place for a future head of state. St Andrews is a convivial university, full of high-class English crumpet. Many of these beautiful burdz dream of being Queen one day. You are, sir, in the words of the St Andrews motto, Sodus Luckius.

St Andrews is also a wonderful base for a sporting prince. The Old Course is right there. Yachting, fishing and canoeing are all at your command. And if Your Premiership wishes to watch high-level soccer, you are only a few miles away from the "Stadium of Light", otherwise known as Central Park, Cowdenbeath. I will be glad to introduce you to the players. In fact, I will be glad to introduce you to the crowd.

Sir, I promise you, life at St Andrews will be all that you could desire, and more. Oh, I forgot to mention work. Is it true that you will be studying the sociology of dysfunctional families? How that could possibly be a suitable training for a member of the royal family I am at a loss to know. I have a set of yellowed lecture notes, which I purchased from another student, and which I am prepared to sell to Your Excellency for whatever number of "bawbees" the market can bear.

Yessir, we St Andreans must stick together.

Annunciations of the Angel of Destiny

It's amateur night at the Harlem Opera House. A skelf of a 16-year-old comes on to the stage. The MC announces: "The next contestant is a young lady named Ella Fitzgerald. Miss Fitzgerald is gonna dance for us....Hold it, hold it. Now, what's your problem, honey? Correction, folks. Miss Fitzgerald has changed her mind. She's not gonna dance, she's gonna sing."

The skinny girl goes on to give three encores. Yet, according to her biographer, she had fully intended to dance that night. But she sang, oh, how she sang! And she never looked back.

It is 1924, and two sisters are singing onstage in Grand Rapids, Minnesota. On toddles their two-year old sister, Frances, to join in the singing. Then Frances sings a solo, "Jingle Bells", which has the audience in raptures. Her father has to haul her offstage. Thus does baby Frances Gumm set out on the faltering journey which is to turn her into Judy Garland. Somewhere, over the rainbow.

H.G. Wells was marked down for a career in the retail trade. He broke his leg when he was eight, and started to read. And read. And write. Albert Einstein didn't speak until he was three: in later life, when he spoke, the whole world listened.

What do these stories mean? Are they simply random happenings? Destiny is such a strange, unaccountable business. There was a special moment when young Ella Fitzgerald decided that she would sing, rather than dance. In that moment, her life path changed. What was it "in her" that made that unplanned choice?

One man who has made an attempt to get "inside" all of this is Jungian psychologist James Hillman, who is rebelling against the received wisdom of the mainstream schools of psychiatry which insist that our fate is determined by our early interactions with our parents. ("They fuck you up, your mum and dad," as Philip Larkin says.)

The iconoclastic Hillman believes that we spend too much time trying to understand our lives by subjecting our psyches to family archaeological digs.

Hillman argues that we are looking in the wrong place. We are each, he says, born with an "image" in our soul, and our life's task is to engage with that "acorn" so that it may grow to its full potential. Plato, in the *Republic,* suggested that the soul of each person is given a unique "daimon" which has selected a pattern that we live on earth. Plato called this explanation a "myth": that is, a story which contains truth.

The Romans gave the name "genius" to the special unique "something". Christians talked about a guardian angel. Even in modern scientific times, the notion has refused to lie down. Various attempts have been made to capture this elusive sense: names such as vocation, destiny, fate and calling appear and reappear.

Modern psychological theories are themselves myths – stories with some truth in them. The trouble is that they present themselves as scientific, "hard" truths providing total explanations. What I find in reading these texts is that they so often seem "dead", flat, and uninspiring. In their quest for objectivity, they squeeze the unique life out of things. They do not really explain how children brought up by the same parents, from the same gene-pool, differ so radically in temperament and gifts.

Maybe the ancient Platonic myth is closer to the heart of the matter. Feelings of destiny can, of course, become dangerous, but there is a "something" about each human being which cannot be reduced to electrical excitations in the brain or explanations in terms of parental conditioning. I have seen people change direction in a way which seems "meant", even though it involves hardship and struggle. In fact, I have known it myself.

You can do things in your life, often apparently unprompted, which produce a "fit", an "aha!" experience. These epiphanies are precious things, intimations of transcendent mysteries for which we cannot find adequate descriptive language. Maybe as parents we worry too much about our children. Could it be that their struggles are often vocational contests, as the inner daimon seeks to find proper expression?

Our adult lives could be transformed and re-energised by reframing them in terms of calling and response. It is not necessarily a calling to a particular job, but to a fully-embodied way of life. Josephine Baker puts it this way: "Is that what they call a vocation, what you do with joy as if you had fire in your heart, the devil in your body?"

There is more to human life than our current theories allow. What we need is not more intense control of our lives, but a radical openness to unexpected annunciations. Turn but a stone and an angel moves: but only if we have eyes to see and ears to hear.

An act which brings the house down

So now we know. Samson was suffering from "antisocial personality disorder". What is even more amazing is that, according to the *Herald,* a "team of Californian psychologists" has been researching the hairy Old Testament giant's case.

If there is anything more scary than Samson, it is a team of Californian psychologists looking for ways to pass the weary hours at someone else's expense. The team, under the leadership of one Eric Altschuler of the University of California at San Diego, breathlessly reveals that Samson demonstrated six of the seven recognised behaviours associated with something called "antisocial personality disorder" (Aspd). Symptoms apparently include impulsiveness, recklessness and habitually getting into fights. (Did this condition originate in Scotland?)

Samson also showed another Aspd symptom, deceit, in that he failed to tell his parents that he got honey from the carcase of a lion. I would be pretty mad myself if my son had killed a lion and hadn't told me. Another dead give-away symptom, apparently is that Samson once killed 1000 Philistines single-handedly with a donkey jawbone and then gloated over his triumph, showing no remorse. I have known school jannies like that.

Samson showed, said the researchers, "an inability to conform to social norms". Nowadays, he would be taken into care. He was also daft enough to tell his Philistine bidie-in, who had already tried to kill him three times, that the secret of his strength lay in his hair. Snip, snip. Gouge out your eyes. Do not pass Go. Once his hair had grown back in, he pulled off the neat trick of hauling down the Philistines' temple, killing thousands of worshipping punters – an action which set back the ecumenical movement hundreds of years.

None of this research comes as any surprise to me, of course. Readers of this column will know that I run a therapy clinic for celebrities in Cowdenbeath, known as the "Friary". Sometimes biblical characters wander in for a bit of counselling and a cooked breakfast. Here is part of a transcript from group therapy session led by my assistant, "Bunny" Culclough.

BUNNY: Samson, after you slaughtered the Philistines with the jawbone of an ass, why didn't you show any remorse?

SAMSON: What's remorse?

DELILAH: It's the way he tells them! (*Much biblical merriment and thigh-slapping.*)

BUNNY: Samson, I think you're in denial.

SAMSON: I'm not in de Nile, I'm in de mire! (*Hysteria breaks out.*)

BUNNY: Any other biblical character with problems?

GOLIATH: Yes. I find that I'm slowing down. I feel leaden-footed and stiff and I creak when I turn.

SAMSON: You must be Cowdenbeath's centre half! (*More thigh slapping.*)

BUNNY: Goliath, your trouble is that your anal-retentive.

JONAH: My problem is that I feel as if I'm surrounded by a big, warm, dark object that I can't shake off. I seem to be travelling all the time, and sometimes I get seasick. Once, a man in a Caledonian MacBrayne uniform asked me for my fare....

BUNNY: Jonah, don't you know that you're in the belly of a whale? What is it that you're running away from? Why do you keep trying to get back to the womb? Why don't you get in touch with your Inner Hero and stand on your own two feet? Are there any addictions or eating disorders here?

PONTIUS PILATE *(with basin and water)*: I can't stop washing my hands. I have to do it every five minutes precisely.

BUNNY: You're suffering from a cleanliness compulsive disorder, Pontius. You need to get out a bit more. Try communing with your Inner Emperor. *(Turns to Samson, who is combing his hair with a garden rake)* Samson, why are you so impulsive and reckless?

SAMSON: I had a difficult upbringing. I behaved badly as a child – forever causing fires, bullying lions, stealing, and winding up the Philistines. I have an antisocial personality disorder. (*Gets up and dances on the table, singing, "If it's good enough for Moses, it's good enough for me."*)

BUNNY: You're barking, Samson. You should be on the stage – you'd bring the house down!

(On hearing these words, Samson rises angrily from his chair, his head touching the ceiling, his outstretched hands grasping the door lintels. He lets out an almighty roar, and pulls down the Blue Brazilian embassy. As the dust clears, the biblical characters are seen scoffing whale and chips – all except John the Baptist, who is devouring a locust supper. Pontius Pilate is washing the dust off his

43

hands.)

You can see from this excerpt just how illuminating it is to have characters from the Bible psychoanalysed thousands of years after the event. Having Samson's id analysed by the odd reveals madness – but whose?

Prickly issue of that cat on the mat

How are things in the theological world these days? This question, I am sure, is always on the lips of all *Herald* readers, and this worthy column, which always has its lug to the philosophical ground, considers it a pleasure – nay privilege – to respond to your incessant pleadings. If you have any metaphysical, theological, scatological or even football questions, the humble, yet scholarly, Kierkegaard of Kirkwall is at your service. So here goes.

The theological world is, as always, in ferment. Impassioned debates go on between liberals, conservatives, Roman Catholics, Prince Charles, Orangemen, The Abominable Snowman, The Eastern Orthodox Church, the Free Kirk, and non-religious groups like the Church of England. The debate ranges across the world, exercising finely-tuned minds from Fife to Fujiyama. I have been exchanging e-mails with theologians in the USA, and intelligence has reached me about an interesting way of crystallising the key issue of scriptural interpretation. The discussion centres around this intriguing question - how would Christians from different church traditions deal with the simple statement, "The cat sat on the mat", if it appeared in the Bible? Here is the Kirkwallian adaptation of the international discussion paper.

Faced with this text, liberal theologians would observe,

urbanely of course, that "the cat sat on the mat" did not mean that a literal cat sat on a literal mat. It would, without question, be a metaphorical cat sitting on a symbolic mat. The Hebrew word translated "cat" would turn out to be a corruption of a word meaning "sacred mushroom". Postmodern theologians would go even further: they would argue that "the cat sat on the mat" was a grand narrative and was thereby disqualified. The Kirk would set up a Special Commission to examine the matter and report back.

At this point, the biblical conservatives would rush in, steam emanating from every orifice. They would insist that it was an essential condition of faith – to be signed in the blood of the martyrs - that a real, physical, living cat did place its whole body on a floor covering, which was "on the floor, but not of the floor", so to speak.

The Reverend Ian Paisley would point out that as "cat" represents the first three letters of "Catholic", a conspiracy must be afoot. A crazed Ayatolla from the Treble Predestinarian Free Kirk would simply crucify a passing moggie to teach the furry sinner a lesson.

Meanwhile, the Roman Catholic Church would announce the Festival of the Sedentation of the Blessed Cat. A gleaming white feline creature would be seated on a purrfect golden rug, while awaiting its assumption to the Great Cat Basket of Heaven. Pilgrims would flock to a shrine at Lochgelly where the bronze Statuary of the Holy Cat would be reported as shedding tears of real blood. A local priest with a church which had a leaking roof would set up a hot dog stall. The festival would be commemorated by the singing of a MagnifiCat, the lighting of seventeen candles, and the ringing of a bell five times. This would inevitably provoke a schism with the Orthodox Church whose tradition would require Holy Cats Day to be marked by lighting eighteen candles, and ringing the bell four times. This holy dispute would be partially resolved by the Cuckoo Land Transvestite Declaration – to be signed only by clergypersons sporting beards and male genitalia – which would cede bits of the sacred city of Bonkle to the Muslim Vegetarian Society of Barking.

The dear old Church of England would predictably get its theological knickers into a twist. The House of Bishops would publish a 999-page report on the Doctrine of the Feline Buttocks. It would explain, in the language of the common people, that in order to determine the "ontological significance of holy cathood", it would follow the analytical principles adopted in dealing with the Feline Fenestration Question (how much is that moggie in the window?). The General Synod would nail its colours firmly to the fence, and the Archbishop of Canterbury, The Rt. Reverend Kenneth Purcell-Dalglish, would say "Mibbes aye, mibbes naw" before commending the report (price £89.99) to lay people puzzled by the difficult doctrine of "the cat sat on the mat".

I hope that all this is perfectly clear. Now that I've offended absolutely everybody, I think I'll clear off. Making jokes about churches is bad for your health and personal security. (By the way, did you know that the anagram of Episcopal is "Pepsi Cola", and that Presbyterian means "best in prayer"?)

For genuine illumination of a dark subject, I leave you with the wise words of Tennyson:

Our little systems have their day;
They have their day, and cease to be;
They are but broken lights of Thee,
And Thou, O Lord, art more than they.

A nation that suffers from split personality

An image has haunted me for the last week and a half. It is of a young Scotsman, with a shaved head, his face contorted with hatred. He is snarling with anger, and the hostility comes bursting through the powerful photograph in the newspaper. There is something about this troubling image which sums up an aspect of Scotland.

Let me sharpen the picture's focus a bit. The young man in question is a footballer, a very talented footballer. He earns thousands of pounds a week. In the blurred background of the photo are masses of football supporters. If you could add stereophonic sound, you would hear a cacophony of hostile noise cascading from the stands. There would be vicious songs of sectarian hatred. The young man, who is shouting at the opposing goalkeeper, is about to be sent from the field.

Freeze-frame the picture, and zoom in on the central figure. Barry Ferguson of Rangers is a young man possessed of a prodigious talent. He has the swagger of a man who has confidence in his ability. He is gallus, and he is entitled to be so. At 22 years old, he is now a pivotal player in the Scottish midfield, and he would command a fee of several million pounds in the transfer market.

Now let the picture move in slow motion. The young man walks off the field, taunted by the opposition supporters. In a last act of defiance, he makes an obscene gesture to the baying Celtic fans. The signal inflames an already volatile situation, and the police and stewards are very anxious. Fortunately, there is no invasion of the pitch.

Fast forward. A few hours later, a young man wearing Rangers colours is involved in a fracas outside a pub. He receives injuries to his face. Barry Ferguson - for it is he - then goes off to join the Scotland squad preparing to play against Latvia in the World Cup. Here's tae us, wha's like us? Damn few, and they're a' deid.

That image from the Old Firm game highlights a contradiction that is at the heart of Scotland. It is the old dichotomy between self-assertion and self-destruction, between the swagger of genuine talent and the cringe of self-loathing, between shouting "We're the greatest" while fearing that we're really the worst. When Craig Brown was manager of Clyde, he had a player in his care who thought a great deal about football, but was a little ponderous in the actual execution of the game. "The trouble with you," Brown told him, "is that your brains are in your heid." The trouble with Barry Ferguson is that all his brains appear to be in his feet.

There's something about the shaved head which accentuates the violence of the Old Firm scene. Down to the bare bone. It's the current fashion, and we may soon have a whole generation of shaved skulls. Nothing wrong with that: the last group of young men with shaved heads I saw was a group of Glasgow monks at the Samye Ling Buddhist monastery in Dumfries. Nevertheless, in certain contexts, the shaved skull is part of a macho, fit-for-Glasgow-kissing style of manhood.

Barry Ferguson troubles me. Unless he screws his

shaved nut his talent will flame and be extinguished like a glorious firework. At the moment, he appears to be acting out an all-too-familiar Scottish script which features precocious gifts, too much money, drink, arrogance, sectarianism, dodgy hangers-on, and violence. On the field, you could see Ferguson lose the plot as Celtic hammered in the goals. Watching him crashing recklessly into tackles, you just knew that it was only a matter of time before he was red-carded. Off the field, it seems, he lost it as well. Ferguson is a winner, though he might yet turn out to be a loser. At the moment, he is both Scotland's glory and Scotland's sickness, an icon of national contradiction. He is MacDiarmid's "Caledonian antisyzygy", or Scottish dualism, in a blue jersey. He is flamboyant leader of the youth section of the Scottish schizoid tendency.

The schizophrenia runs right through the country, from north to south, from east to west. There are other divisions – rich/poor, Protestant/Catholic, rural/urban, public school/state school, but the confidence/inadequacy split is the fundamental psychological fault line which has affected everything else in Scotland for generations. Barry Ferguson certainly didn't create the poison, but it may have contaminated his DNA. I hope not.

There is something in the Ferguson image which is a challenge to Scotland. It is to do with confidence, growing up, and giving up a dark sense of inferiority which manifests itself as graceless swaggering braggadocio. It has to do with economic poverty and poverty of aspiration. It is about throwing away the crutches of tribal hatred and sectarianism, and getting a life.

"There is a storm coming that shall try your foundation," proclaimed Robert Renwick, as he stood on the scaffold in 1668. "Scotland must be rid of Scotland before the delivery come." Can Scotland be rid of Scotland? Can Barry Ferguson be rid of Barry Ferguson?

50

Can our fragile, pilloried parliament – how good we are at sticking the boot into our own! – be part of the solution as well as part of the problem?

And am I reading too much Scottish metaphysics into the simple image of a young man who plies his trade in the blue killing fields of Govan in the year of Our Lord, 2000?

Mibbes aye, mibbes naw, as that other great Scottish footballing icon, Kenny Dalglish would have said. Now there's another tortured Scottish genius, with sparkling, articulate feet. Why are we so good? At schizophrenia?

Honest, Auntie, I've been framed

I t was too much for my Fife auntie. The dear lady goes apprehensively into the newsagents every Thursday, to find out what further damage has been inflicted upon the Ferguson name. She normally reads my column through the spaces between her trembling fingers, wincing as she goes. There are some words in the pieces she dare not even articulate silently.

Last week, she didn't even need to get to my article. There, along the top of the front page of the *Herald*, was a picture of her wayward nephew wearing a crash helmet and leather motorbike gear. The amusing image was part of a trailer for the column inside.

The biker picture had two consequences for me. The first was that of flashback. Some years ago, my wife and I, with our three kids, intended to travel from Iona - where we were then living - to London. The game plan was to get the ferry across the Sound of Iona, then bus it over Mull in time for the 45-minute Cal Mac crossing to Oban. On the Iona ferry, we realised that my wife's handbag, which contained the all-important train tickets, was still in the car on the jetty. What to do? We quickly agreed that she and the kids would get on the bus to Craignure; I would nip back on the ferry and get the handbag, then try to hitch a ride across Mull. It was the only way to get our train.

Hearing of our dilemma, a motorcyclist offered to wait

52

and give me a lift. He had spare gear. So that's how I found myself on the back of this powerful machine, dressed in rubber one-piece suit, crash helmet and goggles, and clutching a handbag.

It turned out to be the motorbike ride from hell. My friendly Samaritan pulled back the throttle, and we raced at 90 miles an hour along the one-track road to Craignure. On corners, the bike leaned over at such an angle that I thought my forehead would skim the road.

I'm sure you don't need me to tell you that terror has a wondrously diuretic effect. I didn't want to stop; but neither did I want to perish the rubber suit. (Auntie, are you still reading this?) I spoke to my friend. He couldn't hear me because of the racket. I tapped him vigorously on the shoulder, and he eventually managed to bring the hurtling bike to a halt. I hopped off, then disappeared speedily into the bushes.

Ah, but human life is not simple. I couldn't undo the zip on the wretched suit. I tugged desperately, without success. Only one thing for it: I had to go back to the bike and get help. So there I was, leader of the esteemed Iona Community, dressed in crash helmet, goggles and rubber suit, clutching a handbag, being unzipped by a similarly attired male. Can you imagine what would have happened if a *Sun* photographer had come round the corner at that precise moment? Don't even think about it.

The other consequence of my photie appearing on the front of last week's *Herald* was that even people who knew me well thought I must be a secret biker. It did my street cred no harm. Some wanted to see my tattoos. Others asked me where I had posed for the picture. Even when I told them the truth - the clever *Herald* designers had taken a photograph from their files, and substituted my sonsie face for that of the world motorcycle champion - they found it hard to disbelieve the evidence of their senses.

Here's where it all gets rather scary. Are the photographs you see in your newspaper authentic? How do you know? Take Tony Blair and Leo. Was the baby really Leo, or newly-born Shuggie McJimsey from Partick? Was it really Tony, or was the prime minister's face grafted on to someone else's body? If you own a digital camera, you will know exactly what I mean. You take a photo, then scan it on to your computer. On screen, you can dress your friends as down-and-outs, and put Maggie Thatcher in beside them. Press "print" - and behold, a beautiful, authentic-looking colour picture.

What you see may not be what you get. The camera can lie. The Soviets used to airbrush inconvenient people out of history; for all we know, it may be happening in spin-doctored Britain right now. El Cid may be dead on his horse, but still animatedly leading today's political cavalry charge.

By the way, I did catch the train to London. That hair-raising journey across Mull was the beginning and end of my motorcycle career. Thanks to the *Herald,* I am now a virtual reality biker. Listen, auntie: have you considered that it's not really me who writes this scurrilous column, that my face has been scanned onto someone else's body?

(Are you still there, auntie-in-agony, or are you, too, an insubstantial creation of the intellectual software of the unreal, real columnist?) From solid old coal-dusted Cowdenbeath to the neon-lit postmodern city of Chimera: it's a short, yet aeons-long, Kierkegaardian journey on a surreal time machine, equipped with kaleidoscopic goggles and numberless, bewildering mirrors.

Warding off the evil eye

A red sky at night is the shepherd's delight: but not when it comes from the funeral pyre of healthy sheep. You can almost choke on the acrid fumes, as they waft apocalyptic messages. But what do they mean?

It was interesting to drive up from Glasgow to Orkney. The car passed over a disinfectant mat near Dalwhinnie. What was it supposed to do? The tyres went over the machine; but what if I had been near a farm on foot? There was no shoe test. Even if there had been, it would not have meant a great deal, since the shoes I was wearing might not have been the ones I had on the day before.

As an exercise in disease prevention, it was largely totemic. It wasn't so much about disinfectant, as about magic. It was a talisman, a way of warding off the evil eye, a despairing attempt to keep the Furies at bay. It was a medieval sign in modern technocratic livery. It was the smearing of innocent lambs' blood on the untouched lintel, a Passover plea, a secular prayer.

We moderns are bound into catastrophic thinking. For all our sophistication, we are continually looking over our shoulder at a shadowy stalker called Fear. As images of the mass burning of animal flesh zoom back and forward through the house of media horrors which we inhabit, the impression is created that Britain is burning.

A catastrophic strain runs through much of our contemporary thinking. It is reinforced by the speed of modern communications and the hysterical selectivity of the "News". Foot-and-mouth. Fuel. Train crashes. Balkans on the brink. When disaster movies and films about demonic possession are thrown into the mix, the heady cocktail of doom will make the calmest heart palpitate.

Below the surface can be detected deep strains of pessimism and, even worse, fatalism. I notice it in conversation time and again: Something is Going to Happen, and there is nothing we can do about it. The script is written.

Our biggest danger lies not in external catastrophes, real or imagined, but in our sense of impotence, our disengagement from what is happening further up the political food chain. I encounter a lot of shoulder-shrugging and resignation, a feeling that nothing can be done about major national events. If it's not gods, it's politicians, and we cannot influence any of them. The die is cast. We are merely bit players in the deterministic cosmic drama.

What this mindset does is to sever the link between individual responsibility and national events. This is the true catastrophe. It is a way of avoiding responsibility, of bodyswerving individual action. Close the curtains and switch on the telly. Anaesthetise despair by living like there is no tomorrow: the apocalyptic hand is already writing the message on the subway walls and there is nothing we can do to influence the result of the endgame.

Our greatest need is not for disaster strategies and emergency plans. It is the need to reconnect: with each other, and with our democratic institutions. Many of the catastrophes we experience are the direct result of leaving things to the "experts", or refusing to make the connections between what we demand, and what is actually happening. What is the link between our worship of the motor vehicle and the threat to our environment? What is the connection between our insistence on year-on-year economic growth and Third World misery? What is the tie between the disintegration of our family structures, and the laying waste of our youngsters' lives through drugs?

Our taking refuge in fatalism makes our prophecies self-fulfilling. This is what the recent Faslane protest was all about. A slide towards nuclear war is not inevitable, yet that tacit assumption is widespread. To leave decisions about the mass slaughter of men, women and children to so-called experts, with their neutral techno-speak, is to turn our backs on what it means to be card-carrying members of the human race.

The transformation that is required is not about finding cleverer technical solutions to difficult problems. Our truly human vocation is to see our neighbour – in the street and at the other end of the world – as a bearer of sacredness. To borrow a metaphor from St Paul's theology of the body of Christ, we are members of one another. If one part of the body suffers, we all suffer. Let me further ransack the Christian mystical tradition, and trace the lineaments of the face of Christ in the poor, the needy and the vulnerable.

The real, costly, horror story of our time is self-obsessive individualism. Beyond the farmyard flames lie the flickering shadows of the transcendent bonfire of our vanities.

A red sky in the morning is the shepherd's warning. The questions are blowing in the wind.

Wake up to the electronic orgasm

I t is a gift from God. An American scientist has
developed an electronic device which provides
orgasms for women at the touch of a button. A gift
from God for women? No, for a columnist. It's impossible
to resist a story from today's techno-fantasy land which
brings together two modern obsessions, sex and
technology.

We live in a time when anybody who does not have
the mandatory 2.6 orgasms a week is regarded as a
dangerous deviant, and when celibates are liable to be
rounded up and sent to re-education camps. It's also a time
when sex is increasingly depersonalised and subjected to
technocratic "solutions" - and when the product of a tennis
star's quick bang with a comparative stranger in a café
broom cupboard is called a "love child".

Which wunderkind is responsible for the electronic
orgasm? Step forward Dr Stuart Meloy, a surgeon from
Winston Salem, North Carolina. The idea for the device
came to him while performing a routine pain-relief
operation on a woman's spine. The procedure involved
planting electrodes and using electrical pulses to modify
pain signals.

"I was placing the electrodes, "said Dr Meloy, "when
the woman suddenly started exclaiming emphatically."
Soon, apparently, it was happy bunny time at the sex farm.

Thus encouraged, Dr Meloy went on to invent a matchbox-sized signal generator that is implanted in one of the patient's buttocks. When the device is connected to certain spinal-chord nerves, the implant triggers an orgasm at will.

"You'd have a hand-held remote control to trigger it," said Dr Meloy, without a trace of a smile. These scientists are a serious lot. According to *New Scientist*, the device can be programmed. Come again? as they say. Clinical trials are to begin later this year with Medtronic, a medical company sited in Minneapolis. A similar device is about to be tested on men.

Don't you just love it? The whole thing has endless possibilities. Supposing, for instance, a woman programmes herself for a certain time in the day, but something goes wrong with the timer. What was intended as a little private coffee-break relaxation would be sure to take the Power Point presentation to 500 business executives by storm. What fun! We could have restaurant scenes straight out of *When Harry met Sally*. A fairly tedious church service could be memorably transformed. (Mind you, the beadle would have to throw the offending lady out. After all, we can't have people screaming "Oh my God!" in the kirk, can we?)

There are household implications as well. Somebody could pick up the TV remote control to switch to *Match of the Day* and innocently spark off an uncontrolled domestic bacchanal which could alarm the dug. Even scratching one's buttocks could have chaotic consequences, especially while asking the boss for a raise.

Electronic devices are notoriously sensitive to outside interference, and a car alarm could activate the orgasm machine. The resultant breathless sound-track could end up being transmitted to a wider public via a taxi cab radio, or through an electronic organ during a funeral service. It all sounds very unPresbyterian to me.

I can now reveal something to you in strictest confidence. A follow-up device has been invented that could allow some unscrupulous person to programme other people's orgasms. How do I know? Well, Dr Meloy was warned in a dream about the awful consequences of such a powerful remote control, and he wisely resolved to pass the only one in existence to a sane, sober and reliable Presbyterian cleric for safe keeping. Naturally, my name was mentioned. So, I have the dangerous prototype buried underground at Skara Brae. (I'm not telling anyone, so keep it a secret, will you?)

Obviously, I won't abuse this trust by activating this machine's horribly fascinating powers. No, I'll only use it on special occasions. I'm not going to tell you which ones, but you'll know soon enough. All I can hint to you is that the General Assembly of the Church of Scotland will be much more fun this year. The Woman's Guild rally will be the most memorable ever. And if the Cardinals are called into conclave to elect a new Pope.....

Politics will not remain unaffected. (Just you watch the next time the pristine Ann Widdicombe advances towards the dark knight of her soul, Michael Howard!) Henry McLeish is going to become less dull, especially when the voluptuous Big Margo is around. And as for the Queen's Christmas broadcast.....

Yes, with one touch of a button I will bring gaiety to the nations. Be assured: you'll be able to see all these things on television. I plan to sell the rights to "pay per view" day-time orgasms - with recorded highlights at night – to that nice Mr Murdoch. You'll love it! Watch, though, how you use the remote control.

To demonise abusers is to miss the point

Monster. According to the *Concise Oxford Dictionary* it means "Mis-shapen animal or plant, abortion; imaginary animal compounded of incongruous elements, e.g. centaur, sphinx, griffin; inhumanly wicked person, inhuman example; animal, thing, of huge size." To monsterize someone is to place him or her beyond the human pale.

The crime of abuse of innocent children is a truly horrendous one, and it's little wonder that people range along the extreme boundaries of human language in trying to speak about it. It's not hard to understand how this vile crime arouses such violent passions. It is also entirely right that all reasonable steps should be taken to ensure that children are protected.

What is untruthful is the pretence that those guilty of these offences are not of us, bone of our bone, flesh of our flesh. The attempt to externalise evil does not work. The wardens of the Nazi death camps were not members of another species; they were, many of them, family men who went home to wives and children and played Beethoven. They were human beings capable of utterly inhuman behaviour.

Paedophiles are not from a different planet. Part of the reason they make us shudder is that they hold up a mirror to humanity, and we recoil from what we see. They are living reminders of the depth and extent of human evil.

Now I'm not about to do the bleeding-heart liberal bit about everybody being the same, and we're all responsible for everything that happens, and so on. Most human beings are not inclined to abuse and murder. Yet twentieth century Europe has been a vast human slaughterhouse in which huge numbers of civilised human beings have inflicted primitive and sadistic offences on fellow members of their race. It has been the century of the ovens, the gulag, the torture chamber, the killing field; all to the sound of music. The perpetrators – not just the British ones – are "us". To monsterize them and keep alive the comforting illusion that they are not really humans is a self-serving evasion.

A convicted paedophile was in my house not long ago; he eventually left his home because he could not handle the hostility. I have sympathy with parents who are concerned about the safety of their children; if I had grandchildren, I would not wittingly let them near some of the people I have encountered. Yet to knowingly demonise paedophiles and to unleash the mob is to commit a different kind of crime against humanity. It is also, paradoxically, to make children less safe.

The rioting people who burned and smashed houses, who caused one man to commit suicide, who hounded innocent people out of their homes and who drove the "monsters" underground were not the worst offenders. The people who should be in the dock are the proprietors of the *News of the World*. They are not fools. They, of all people, know that words are like weapons, and their protestations of innocence have a very hollow ring. They remind me of Ian Paisley, who trumpets that he is against violence while releasing verbal incendiaries which ignite in the brains of less sophisticated followers. The sales-driven tabloid hysteria is as cynical as it gets.

The unpalatable truth is that innocent children are much more at risk in their own homes than they are on the streets. Remember the hysteria over Louise Woodward ("England's Rose")? At the same time as the tabloids were "saving" Louise – as she was always sweetly referred to – a man in Aberdeen was being sent down for 25 years for the murder of a child. The mob bayed "scum" and "animal"; yet both Woodward and Steven Leisk, after due process of law, had been declared responsible, in one way or another, for the death of a child. It is right that Leisk should be kept away from children for life; but this "monster" was himself a pathetic human being. Brutally abused as a child, he was traumatised by his work as a medical orderly in the Falklands war, clearing up dismembered bodies.

Around five children are murdered by strangers each year. That is five too many. Yet, current hysteria notwithstanding, that figure has remained static for the last 30 years. By far the biggest problem is abuse within the family and child-care institutions. It is preferable to attack strange "monsters" in the street than to face this hideous reality.

Another statistic: around 200 children are killed by motor vehicles in Britain every year. Will the *News of the World* name and shame speeding drivers who put children's lives at risk? Will there be mobs at the doors of "outed" drivers? Of course not. The *News of the World* is too busy crusading for cheaper petrol – and, besides, a lot of its readers have cars.

Tony Blair has written to poor Sarah Payne's parents. "If there's anything I can do for you, let me know," said the prime minister. I'm sorry to be cynical, but can I take it that a similar letter was sent to the family of 12-year-old

Emma Hall (uncelebrated, unlamented in public) who was killed in her own home by her father?

What are the chances of seeing political leadership with steel in its spine, one whose agenda is not driven by tabloids, mobs, fashions and focus groups? It's time to call the baying lynch mobs off the streets, and tackle the real problem – which, sadly, is much nearer to home.

Chants would be a fine thing to resume

Well I never! Here is the great new advance in education – chanting by pupils. They apparently learn better when they chant things out. I wonder how many think-tanks and consultants fees went into re-inventing that particular wheel.

I can well remember chanting the tables. Not only that, I can still, on good days, do mental arithmetic. A lot of today's kids are counted out if the battery in the calculator goes flat. Even the simplest of sums can't be done.

Another thing I recall is the memorising and reciting of poetry. Most of these poems can still be rescued from the memory traces. In fact, great lines come unbidden to my mind. How I loved the gorgeous, evocative language of *The Ballad of Sir Patrick Spens:*

The king sits in Dumferling toune
Drinking the blude-reid wine.

Us Cowdenbeathians, sitting in the shadow of the capital of the kingdom of Fife, had a little parody

The king sits in Dunfermline Glen
Chewing the end of his ballpoint pen.

The thing about parody is that you need to know the original. It saddens me that so few youngsters know classical poetry by heart. And you can forget about the *Authorised Version of the Bible,* or Shakespeare. The very notion of great literature is savaged by barbarians dressed up as university lecturers. Our culture is dying of memory loss.

This learning of poetry can go awry, mind you. My mother, as a schoolgirl, loved to recite "The Laird o' Cockpen, he's prood and he's great": until, that is, someone pointed out that she hadn't got it quite right when she declaimed: "The Laird o' Cockpen, he spewed ow'er his grate."

Children love chanting. Rhythmic oral speech forms neural pathways in the brain. The youngsters who did well in the research project were taught to chant mantras like "I will become a very good reader" and "I like books, books are fun". I can understand the power of this. Learning has a lot to do with attitude and belief.

Scotland has a poor track record in building self-esteem among pupils. When I went to St Andrews University I felt intimidated by the English public school graduates with their polished accents and easy, born-to-rule manner. Some of them affected not to understand this creature from darkest West Fife, and I was inhibited by their confidence and style. Yet some of them were less bright than the locals, who had sadly been taught that speaking up in class was a sign of big-headedness. "He's got a right guid conceit of himsel'" can be a crippling Scottish condemnation. Positive thinking is something we could do more of in Scotland. We need to start with the children.

A word of caution, though: the affirmations need to be credible. I am bombarded with literature which assures me that by following this or that course I can have the future I want, the health I want, the job I want, the income I want. With the right techniques, I am solemnly assured, I can control my bit of the universe. All I need to do, apparently, is have the right affirmations and visualisations.

While we could use some more possibility thinking, this extreme form of hubris is very damaging. It acknowledges no limitations; thus, disillusion is bound to set in. Those who fail to usher in an all-singing, all-dancing personal future are doubly damned; not only are they personally inadequate, they are condemned for not believing enough as well.

I have seen this kind of demoralising effect with illness. Desperate patients with terminal cancer are told by gurus that if they have enough faith, they will be cured. While a positive attitude can have an effect on the course of illness, patients who don't 'succeed' not only have to contend with the illness itself, but with the self-accusation that they have accelerated their own death by a failure of belief. This is a form of cruelty.

Life has possibilities, but also boundaries. We are not in charge of our own destinies, despite the all-conquering rhetoric. I often encounter a poster which features birds in flight, and bears the legend, "They fly because they think they can". Wrong. They fly because they have wings. Down through history there have been people who thought they could fly unaided: they are called dead people.

So I want to give two cheers for chanting. The humble bumblebee does defy all the known laws of aerodynamics. How it gets its wee tartan bum airborne is, apparently, a divine mystery. The unpretentious creature flies because God has a sense of humour. And as it buzzes around with a smile on its daft wee face, it chants, "I'm the best wee bumblebee in the world".

Liberal polyfilla that damages the brain

L isten to this important text for the new era. It's worthy of close attention. "Graduates will soon be half the population, so Tories will be educated out of existence. To be liberal is to be free of superstition and irrational fear, open to the new, optimistic about the future, knowing there has never been a better time to be alive than now."

The author of this wondrous drivel is Polly Toynbee, columnist for the *Guardian* newspaper. This Polly-in-Wonderland paragraph is a key scripture in the contemporary cultural canon, and is therefore worthy of close biblical exegesis and a bit of deconstruction.

Where to begin? Ms Toynbee's words are riddled with dogmas which are simply assumed. Liberals, of course, never have anything as crude as dogmas. All educated people, it seems, simply know that these things are true. This is smug liberalism at its ghastliest.

The first little dogma is that no educated person can be a Tory. Now, I must confess that out of all the mainstream political groupings, the Tory party is the one I feel least drawn to. I concede that this has as much to do with upbringing and instinct as to philosophical argument. Yet the *Guardian* writer's inference that no educated person can be a Tory is itself an illustration of how stupid educated people can be. Whatever you make of it, the Conservative philosophy is a coherent and persistent one. At its best, it is about the conservation of things, ideas, and attitudes that are felt to be of enduring value.

Let's take it out of the philosophical realm and think of real, flesh-and-blood people. Here's a really outstanding Scottish example - the late Sir Alick Buchanan-Smith (another of our finest political leaders to die at a grievously young age.) He was a thoughtful, decent, able man of great personal integrity, who did what so few ministers seem to do nowadays – resign from office as a matter of principle. He was one of the few to face down Margaret Thatcher and tell her that she was wrong.

The problem with the Tories is that for every Sir Alick there are three William Hagues. The political skinhead's populist flirting with the philosophical fringes of the British National Party is both pathetic and dangerous. Even so, the assertion that the Tories "will be educated out of existence" is an arrogant piece of intellectual Pollyfilla.

On to the next bit from the Toynbee script for the liberal *Sound of Music*. "To be liberal is to be free of superstition and irrational fear." Eh?

This is Pollyana time. Surely you would have to be on very wacky baccy to write this stuff? This is the kind of slogan that used to appear on walls in Eastern Europe – with "communist" substituted for "liberal" - under great posters of gleaming workers with flags. These 1950s sentiments had the same connection to reality as Polly-through-the-looking-glass's imagining that she is seeing the world when, in fact, she is staring at the reflection of her own benign liberal face.

In my experience, people who make a lofty point of calling themselves liberal turn out to be as dogmatic, irrational, and intolerant as anyone else. Against apartheid, yes: against economic exploitation, of course: but put some probing questions about, say, abortion, and the molars are soon flashing and temple veins throbbing.

It goes without saying that among the high-priests of liberalism, all religion is "superstition" and deep conviction is suspect. (Except, of course, the deep conviction that political and cultural liberalism is the way, the truth and the life.)

Gee, it must be great to live so free of superstition and irrational fear! And, of course, to be "open to the new, optimistic about the future, knowing there has never been a better time to be alive than now." This sounds like the kind of hypersonic, brain-endangering Islington guff that Tony Blair spouts at the orchestrated evangelical New Labour love-ins which masquerade as party conferences. In order to be believed, it has to be delivered with fervour, sweaty shirt, and flashing white wallies against a background of Mary Poppins music. Yes, this is a good time to be alive – if you are white, educated, employed and living in the western world. Otherwise, it may be fairly hellish.

At its finest, liberal democracy delivers many good things, especially in the area of the defence of individual liberties. Its track record here is excellent. But liberalism's biggest distortion is that it makes the happiness and fulfilment of the autonomous individual adult its moral and spiritual benchmark, no matter the consequences. And there is no one quite so illiberal as a liberal whose "self-evident truths" are subjected to close scrutiny.

Ms Toynbee: educated you may be, but isn't it time you used your brains?

Conspiracy of silence about death

H ave you faced up to your own death recently?
That's the cheery wee question from the
meenister today. This regular spot in the *Herald* is
not one of these frivolous columns centring on domestic
trivia, or ephemeral things like politics. This is a
Presbyterian column. It's not about enjoyment. It's about
things like, well, death. Or foot-and-mouth. Or pestilence.
Stuff like that. Important stuff.

Well, have you? Have you faced up to your own death
recently? Did you look in the bathroom mirror this
morning and say to the lugubrious image looking back at
you: "You, pal, are going to die. Think about it." Indeed, on
any given morning, you may look like death and feel like
death. In fact, you may even be dead.

A week or two ago, I did a wee talk to the nation on
the subject of Søren Kierkegaard and death. It was
broadcast at 8.30am on a Sunday morning. How many of
the nation, I wondered aloud as I frightened my own self in
the mirror, would be all set to jump out of their secular,
nay debauched, pits early on a Sunday morning shouting,
"Quick. Switch on the wireless! It's Kierkegaard on death!"
(I once preached on the general topic in St Magnus
Cathedral on a bright summer's morning, and when I
announced the theme to the eagerly expectant

71

holidaymakers, no less a personage than Sir Jock Slater, First Lord of the Admiralty, groaned out loud, "Oh, God!" How do I know? His wife shopped him, that's how.)

Well, let me tell you, a lot of people listened to that broadcast. I know, because I was inundated with letters. Am I exaggerating? Yes, of course. Clergy always exaggerate, even the very upright ones. (Try it out – ask a cleric how many people regularly attend his services. The lie begins with a modest little cough.) Anyway, the postie's bag groaned with Kierkegaard and death.

Talk of death today is avoided like foot-and-mouth. Oh, yes, there are lots of jokes about it, but serious speech about death is noticeable by its peculiar absence. In the Victorian era, talk of death was plentiful, but sex was taboo. Now it's the other way around.

Easter brings a sharp focus to such personal, existential issues. Like no other season, it raises explosive questions about mortality, life and belief. It is a time for reflection on the heart of the matter.

It is appointed unto all men once to die, says the old scripture, going straight for the metaphysical jugular. There is only one way out of this life. All sorts of things may be variable and unpredictable, but not this one. Death, in other words, is a part of life. Yet there is a conspiracy of silence about it.

Because death is inescapable, every person must establish a meaning for his or her own death. If you see death as the end of everything, that will affect how you live your life. If you see death as the doorway to a new life, that will also have an impact upon you. If you spend all your time dreading death, or become obsessed by death, that will distort your day-to-day existence. And if you simply avoid the issue and sweep it under the carpet, it will come up and confront you in most unexpected ways. In other words, if you are to live well and fully, you need to acknowledge the unavoidable fact of your own death, and find a meaning for that event that you can live with.

Part of our contemporary problem – and hence the uneasy silence – is that we have lost any transcendental context for death. It is largely taken as read that all talk of a larger context is wishful thinking. But this modern cultural script is itself riddled with questionable assumptions.

Here is a mysterious story about death, one which refuses to be shaken out of our history.

It is a Thursday evening. A man is in an upper room with his friends. He takes bread and breaks it. This is my body, broken for you. He takes wine and pours it. This is my blood, shed for you. I will not drink of the fruit of the vine until I drink it new in the kingdom of God.

The good man goes out, to be handed over, to be delivered to death. He will be executed by church and state as an outlaw. Darkness will cover the land.

But a light will come, and come again. It will illumine the bleak landscape of our woundedness, and our dreadful losses. The runic writing on Black Friday's walls will stammer the daring truth that there is a beyondness to all things: and that its Sunday name is grace.

That Christmas newsletter again

*H*i, everybody! Well, it's this time of year again! I simply can't believe it'll soon be Santa time. How the years fly by! We're all getting older, I suppose! Anyway, it's time to give you the Stoneywood family news once more. I always look forward to letting you know how we're all getting on. Apologies for using the standardised letter, but it makes life easier.

Well, this has been another successful year for the Stoneywood family. Jim has had a good year, but I'll let him tell you all about it. As for me, I was promoted to the post of principal teacher of mathematics at the school. As you know, I've worked really hard at improving my skills, and I don't mind saying that I deserved the promotion. Some of the teachers are, to put it bluntly, lazy. In fact, the staff room is full of moaning slobs. They should really all take a course in positive thinking!

There are a lot of slovenly youngsters in the school, but, despite it all, I try to remain bright and cheerful. It's the only way. You have to rise above it all if you're going to get anywhere in life, that's what I always say. You see, the glass of life is half full, not half empty!

I wish I could get that message through to Mum. She's always complaining about the home she's in, and it drives me potty. The food's never right, the temperature's never right, the staff are always terrible. She complains all the time about her hip and her colostomy and her poor eyesight, and she keeps saying that she wishes she were dead. I keep telling her that there are many people worse off than she is, and that she's got *lots* to look forward to. Some people always look on the black side. It's important not to surround yourself with negative people.

The family are all doing terribly well. Jonathan had another successful year. He's still working in the City, and making lots of money, as usual. He and Tamsin are expecting a new sprog, so that'll be another addition to the Stoneywood clan!

Julian has had a very successful year, I'm glad to say. He's in his final year at Edinburgh, and looks set for a First Class Honours degree.

Claire got straight As in twelve subjects. Didn't she do well? She's now at Cambridge, reading Classics and Philosophy. And Samantha's doing well at school – she looks like being another star! Don't your family make you feel proud? Anyway, I'll let Jim take over....

Hello! As Amy says, this has been another brilliant year for the Stoneywoods. My job goes on from strength to strength. Amy has filled you in on the progress of the offspring, so I won't say any more, other than to add that they're a credit to the clan. My Mum has had another successful year, even though Dad died so tragically after he fell into the septic tank. The only thing that worries me about Mum is that she's gone all hippy-ish. She's started wearing clothes suitable for someone much younger than her years, and she's reading all kinds of weird things. She goes to yoga classes every week, as well as a course on something called "Tantric love making", whatever that might be. She's turned vegetarian, and she's also started drinking a glass of her own urine every day. Honestly! Apparently, some Indian gurus do it. Mum insists it does her good. It hasn't improved her breath, but I can't find a delicate way of telling her.

I did have a bit of a scare with Mum, to be honest. I was sitting having a glass of Chardonnay with her while she sipped her urine. She suddenly fell to the floor, clutching her chest. I panicked, and started giving her the kiss of life – terrible taste! – when she cocked one eye open and said, "I'll bet that gave you a bit of a fright!" Fright? I was so bewildered I downed her urine by mistake in one go. She told me she had done it deliberately "to shake my complacency". Honestly! If worry weren't such a negative thing, I'd worry about her.

Tammy the dog has also had a good year, despite losing a leg after an accident with the lawn mower. I didn't see him bounding up behind me in the garden, and when I turned round, bingo, his front left leg had gone AWOL. He has coped with the adversity in typical Stoneywood manner – by treating it as a growth experience. He never complains.

Ginger had a learning experience as well. He was chased by a dog across the road and was run over by a Mercedes. Ginger always had class! We'll miss him.
Oh, Hammy the hamster had a growth experience too. You'll remember in our last Christmas newsletter we told you that we'd bought a hamster for Samantha for her birthday. Well, a few months ago, Hammy became quite depressed. We took him to the vet, who told us that poor Hammy had lost his hearing as a result of an ear infection.

Darling Samantha, ever inventive, "borrowed" her grandmother's hearing aid so that Hammy could still enjoy his favourite programme *Who wants to be a Millionaire?* She hooked Hammy up and switched on, whereupon there was an almighty explosion. We're still finding bits of dear Hammy behind furniture of the living room, but each find reminds us of the hidden treasures of life.

So, apart from one or two minor difficulties, it's been another good year for the Stoneywood clan. As a family, we're always reaching toward new goals. I hope our newsletter has helped and inspired you, as you reflect on your own family successes. Remember our Christmas message: the glass of life is half full, not half empty! Stay in touch!

Love,

Jim, Amy, Jonathan, Julian, Claire, Samantha and Tammy.

Buggered santa beggars belief

When I was, as they say in Orkney, a peedie boy, Santa Claus used to come to Cowdenbeath for a month. In those days, the town was run by two organisations, the Labour party and Cowdenbeath Co-operative Society, known as "The Store".

The Co-op was not based on Marxist doctrine, but on simple community ideals. Ordinary members of the public became shareholders in "The Store", and everybody in the town seemed to belong. Each person had a Store number, and every quarter a dividend was paid out. The day the "Divvy" was disbursed was always exciting; a long queue would snake along the pavement from early morning as people talked animatedly about what they would spend their share of the profits on.

Anyway, there was only one place where Santa Claus could be resident in Cowdenbeath – The Store. On the first day of December, Mr Claus was put on the train in Dunfermline, and six minutes later, he arrived at Cowdenbeath railway station. (These were the days before RailTrack. Nowadays, the train would languish for hours in a siding, if it hadn't actually turned upside down on the track.)

Schools always finished early that day. The platform at Cowdenbeath railway station was thronged with cheering children as Santa alighted from the train. He then made his way on foot through the smiling punters, past the football ground, and up to the Co-op.

At home, all four of us young kids believed in Santa Claus. I can remember exactly when the first doubts began to surface. We had watched Santa arrive at the station, and had walked along High street behind him. There was ice on the pavements, and at one point, Santa slipped and fell. No problem with that.

The philosophical excitement began later, when my elder sister breathlessly revealed that she had been very close to Santa when he stumbled, and that he had said a "bad word". Under interrogation, Mary revealed that the benign and jolly red-coated saint had exclaimed, "bugger!"

Lapland, reindeer and narrow chimneys accommodating a rotund gentleman we could cope with. But the notion of a Santa who said "bugger" imposed some strains on the metaphysics of it all. It was hard to get one's tiny Fife mind around it. It was, as they say in the rough old theological trade, a version of the theodicy question. How could a good Santa - who only came, we were assured, to boys and girls who were well behaved – utter bad words? And in Cowdenbeath High Street, of all places? The world was suddenly turned upside down, and I was invaded by existential angst. No wonder I took up later with Mr Kierkegaard.

I thought of all that this week when I read that children watching a Christmas procession in Great Yarmouth dissolved into tears when a man dressed as Santa was handcuffed and arrested by police for punching a teenager. What troubled them most was that Santa might be banged up in a cell over Christmas.

Some will see this as a further argument in favour of abolishing Santa Claus and levelling with children. I don't think so. We're already stealing bairns' childhoods. They can't play anywhere. They're stuck in front of a screen and told to shut up. By the time they're three they're being told how to use condoms and the morning-after pill. To take away a bit of the magic and sentiment of the Christmas season in order to live in a more politically correct and "rational" universe would be a further step towards bleakness.

Rigorous Christians will tell me that if Santa and all the Christmas trappings are abolished, more attention will be focused on the Bible story. Do they really believe that? Signed-up atheists will tell me that Santa should be given his P45 because the whole story encourages the kind of credulity which supports belief in a God who is, they assure me, no more than a projection of human need. This reductionist argument works both ways. It is just as plausible to say that an atheist is conditioned not to believe in God because it's more comfortable not to face the disturbing possibility of judgment.

I've never found Christianity to be a particularly easy religion. And the old theodicy question is intractable: how can a good God allow suffering? There is no earthly answer to this; but a wistful blood-red story, beginning at Bethlehem, provides an alternative, less imperial, reading of the universe.

In the meantime, I still hang up my stocking at Christmas. Nowadays, I can cope with a Santa who says "bugger", provided he does the business. I look no more to Mr Claus for perfection, but turn instead to Our Leader, Mr McLeish, for words of wit and wisdom. Yes, progressive pragmatism: that's what growing up is all about.

Latest tidings from Dumbadoon

This worthy column does not flinch in its task of reporting advances in the great surge forward of civilisation. Are you ready for the latest dispatch from the progressive trenches? This may be strong meat for breakfast time, but here it is: very soon, at a video shop near you, there will be films on general UK release which will feature "masturbation and close-up shots of penetration and ejaculation."

Hey, don't sit too near the screen! You have been warned. Welcome to 21st century Britain.

This massive evolutionary step forward was announced by the British Board of Film Classification. They have changed the rules about what can be shown on R18 classified videos. From now on, "more detailed scenes can be shown using genitals, fingers, the tongue or sex aids." And, presumably, toes, used copies of the *Sunday Post*, and dyno-rods. Sex rules, OK? Mind you, primary school kids won't be able to see the films. Not yet, anyway. The new guidelines were drawn up because of successful legal challenges to the cutting of some explicit sex scenes from films titled - wait for it - *Horny Catbabe, Office Tart*, and *Nympho Nurse Nancy*. We're not talking Shakespeare here.

Something about the titles tells me that these films

weren't produced by the Kirk. Or even by the Women's Institute. (Though you can't be sure about the WI nowadays. How long before we get *The WI Horny Middle-Aged Catbabes' Calendar*?)

This latest thrilling advance in civilisation surely confirms that we humans are much more enlightened than animals. After all, rabbits aren't sophisticated enough to sit round a TV on Friday evenings watching close-ups of other rabbits simulating copulation. They're too busy out there doing it. (Or am I showing my ignorance here? Have things really changed that much since I last watched David Attenborough?)

As human beings, we are distinguished from other creatures by the ability to reflect on such matters as sex, life and death; and *Nympho Nurse Nancy* - with knee-trembling close-ups - is, as they say in Lochgelly, part of a creative, synergetic, evanescent vortex of neo-primitive erotic cadences. Och aye.

Actually, it's impossible to approach a television screen nowadays without the familiar sights and sounds of writhing, screaming and ejaculating - and that's just *Match of the Day*. Every night brings the Synchronised Hairy-Arsed Bobbing Olympics on Channel 5, that flagship of the new cultural dawn. (This is the channel that thinks that the 9 o'clock watershed is where you park your rowing boat at night.) It is impossible to send it up. What you see on the TV screen nowadays is the kind of stuff that can put a conscientious, law-abiding satirist out of business.

I recently wrote a piece about the dumbing-down of television drama, particularly on Channel Four. The response was interesting. One senior Scottish film producer wrote to me to share his despair about the sheer level of ignorance among the trendy young execs who call the shots about film projects. When I wrote the article, I didn't know that Channel Four was about to launch its

82

latest sensational Big Idea.

For those of you living in caves without newspapers, the Big Brother programme features ten strangers cooped up in a flat for nine weeks. Twenty-five cameras and microphones follow all their movements - even their bowel movements. Breathless voyeurs who simply can't get enough are able to follow the action 24 hours a day on the internet. Each week, one of the happy campers will be voted out of the flat by the viewers. The sole remaining person will win a £70,000 prize.

The narcissistic volunteers - what is truly depressing is that they were chosen out of 20,000 applicants - were selected largely because of their youthful good looks. Those who are ejected each week will be offered "counselling" in order to deal with the problems of rejection by a mass audience. (One reject inconveniently committed suicide when the show was produced in Holland.) The greatest excitement in the European run was that two of the cast were caught on camera having sex! Wow! One of the Channel Four programme directors admitted that a similar happening here would do the ratings no harm. Of course, the programme isn't sold in that way.

"Big Brother is a bold enterprise," said Stevan Keane, a spokesman for Channel Four. "It places the channel at the forefront in exploring new ways of marrying the two most powerful media."

This vacuous drivel comes straight from the cultural handbook of the increasingly dominant domain of Dumbadoon, whose tedious civic clique consists of mediocre luvvies who manage to give superficiality a bad name. Under their brain-dead leadership, we are in danger of becoming a nation of spiritless voyeurs – jaded, dirty raincoat saddos, flicking aimlessly through multiple TV channels, immobilised by ennui. We are in a downwardly-mobile cultural trance.

83

Still, *Office Tart* (with close-ups) will soon be available to provide a hyped Happy Hour. We will be invited to boogie on down with Nympho Nurse Nancy. Listen to the music of the age: dumb, dumb, dumbdie dumb.

The jewelled garden beyond the boundaries of time

A s I stand on the embankment looking over the beach, it is an idyllic picture. The sun is shining, the sea is sparkling, and laughing youngsters are running along the sand. It is a glorious Orkney June day. I want to freeze-frame that picture for the moment, and come back to it shortly.

The summer Orkney light never ceases to take my breath away. I particularly like the long evenings, when the wind drops and everything goes still. It will soon be the longest day, when people will play golf at midnight, celebratory hipflask in and out of pocket. If it is a clear night, folk will read the *Orcadian* on their doorstep at the bewitching hour. Then, after three hours or so of shadowy darkness, the sunlight will be streaming through the windows again.

If you go out walking late, you enjoy the big sky. (I now feel claustrophobic in the city. You can't see a horizon. And if you smile at people in the street, they avert their eyes, wondering what's wrong with you. What are we doing to each other?) But even as you walk in the evening Orkney sunlight, you know in your Scottish Calvinist soul that things will soon change. I love the piece by Alastair Reid:

It was a day peculiar to this piece of the planet, when
larks rose on long thin strings of singing and the air shifted
with the shimmer of actual angels. Greenness entered the
body. The grasses shivered with presences and sunlight
stayed like a halo on hair and heather and hills.

Walking into town, I saw, in a radiant raincoat, the
woman from the fish-shop.

"What a day it is!" cried I, like a sunstruck madman.
And what did she have to say for it? Her brow grew bleak,
her ancestors raged in their graves as she spoke with their
ancient misery:

"We'll pay for it, we'll pay for it, we'll pay for it!"

Aye. Right enough. Soon, the days will start to turn.
Orcadians always reckon that intimations of winter begin
with the County Show, held on the second Saturday of
August. That's the day when the beasts are in their finery,
and Orkney is in festive mood for its biggest agricultural
jamboree. This year, for the first time in half a century,
Bignold Park will be silent, victim to the fear of pestilence.
Aye, we'll pay for it.

And the days will lengthen, and the daylight will flee.
The summer evenings will be a distant memory as the
December sky darkens in the early afternoon. You will
learn again what a black night sky really looks like, except
on the rare occasions when the merry dancers put on their
son et lumière show.

But back to that ridge above the beach, down beside
the third Churchill barrier. What is happening below is our
Sunday School picnic. Was the template for that annual
ritual established on Mount Sinai? Or did it go further
back to the days when Jacob's twelve Hebrew weans went
for a trip? We have buses now instead of camels, but the
sacred pattern endures – sandwiches, races, football
matches in which middle aged men render serious injury to
themselves and others. When I was about seven years old,

I prayed to Jehovah that I would win the egg-and-spoon race at the Sunday School picnic. I came in last. I was an atheist for at least four years.

As I look at the scene, in all its happiness and innocence, set against such a glorious backdrop, it has a paradisiac feel.

Then I remember why I am leaving the picnic early. I am going to conduct the funeral of a man who has been brutally murdered in Kirkwall. This same man, from a fine Orkney family, once himself ran races at Sunday School picnics, played football for Orkney, represented the Boys' Brigade at sports events.

The translucent Orkney light has been invaded by bleak darkness.

There is no way back to Eden. The route is closed for fear of spreading pestilence. There is no perfect, idyllic community on this earth. None. While we rightly long to visit Utopia, it inevitably turns out to be a dangerous, even murderous place. And the sunlight of our individual lives is invaded by our own shadows.

What are we doing to each other? We will, it seems, pay for it, till the end of time. Yet, there are subversive rumours of angels: and wild stories of a wounded stranger paying for it, bringing light into the darkest shadows, pointing forward to a jewelled garden beyond the boundaries of time.

With reluctance I turn my back on the scene, and switch on the ignition of the car.

The
Short
Stories

Hitler was a vegetarian

T am Pollock remembered it in the way people can say
exactly what they were doing when they heard the
news that President Kennedy had been shot. It was
at six minutes past two in the afternoon of twenty second
September nineteen hundred and eighty two, while eating
a bacon roll in Tognarelli's Cafe in Lochgelly – as the juke
box played 'Stand By Your Man' – that the information
exploded in his brain: Adolf Hitler, Fuhrer of the Third
Reich, was a vegetarian.

Tam had been reading an article in the *Courier*
recounting Hitler's rise to power fifty years previously. The
writer had remarked casually, in a throwaway subordinate
clause, that Hitler did not eat meat. The phrase startled,
then seared him.

At first he would not believe it, but a frantic
ransacking of the Fuhrer's biographies in Lochgelly Public
Library confirmed the news. Hitler had indeed been a
vegetarian.

Tam had been slightly uneasy about vegetarians for as
long as he could remember. Nothing he could pinpoint,
mind you. Veggies were thin on the ground in West Fife,
but they still disturbed him. The very mention of lentils and
beansprouts could give him a migraine. There was
something strangely distasteful about people who refused
to eat good solid meat. The revelation about Hitler merely

brought to the surface his latent suspicions and fears.

Tam asked his friends in Lochgelly if they knew that Hitler had been a vegetarian. Some affected disinterest, most were surprised, a few even stunned.

"It was his reverence for life," remarked Joe McGurn, ever the joker. Tam was not amused. It was not a subject for laughter.

Tam, who had been made redundant four years previously at the age of 41 when the last pit in the area had closed, spent more and more of his waking hours in the library. (His mother was amazed - and pleased - that he was now getting up in the morning. She had been worried by his apathy and by his appearance - filthy bunnet on top of matted long hair, stubbled and mottled face, perpetual dead roll-up dangling from the lips.) He studied biographies of contemporary politicians, searching for incriminating evidence. He would go through the index first, then scan the pages. The notion of a Vegetarian Plot was forming in his mind.

His secret researches took him farther and farther away from the bleak West Fife landscapes. He even went on a day trip to the Mitchell Library in Glasgow. But it was in Fife, in the Carnegie Public Library, Dunfermline, that he found the evidence he wanted at ten thirty in the morning of twenty seventh October, nineteen hundred and eighty three. Page 245 of Denis Mack Smith's life of Benito Mussolini contained the information that the consumption of meat had decreased sharply in Italy in the 1930s, and that the Italian dictator, "who was himself inclined to vegetarianism, expressed pleasure that twenty million Italians were now having to follow his example."

So the butchers of Europe were vegetarian! A thrill went through the Lochgelly man. He read and reread the words, then read them again. As he pondered these things in his heart, the conspiracy theory hardened in his mind.

Now there could be no doubt. There had been - and undoubtedly still was - a vegetarian plot to wipe out the carnivores of Europe. How had no one ever seen it?

He told no one, not even his mother. He simply asked the old lady to increase the amount of meat in his diet. He wanted to fortify himself. She was surprised, because she already gave Tam a lot of meat, more than could reasonably be afforded from their combined income of old age pension and unemployment benefit. Steak pie, lamb chops, chicken, veal, stew and stovies became even more strongly represented on the weekly menu. Tam savoured every bit, preparing himself for what must come.

The signs multiplied. Vegetarian recipes were seen daily in the papers. Even the *Courier*. The people were weakening. Diet experts were forever on television, promoting the anti-meat campaign. Why, oh why, had no one seen it? Tam observed what he took to be vegetarian handshakes exchanged by Fife bank managers. So international capitalism was suspect! Was monetarism a code-word? Tam shovelled in more stovies, fuel.

It was while at a singles disco at Cardenden that Tam found a soul mate, a comrade for the struggle. While having a pint and a steak pie at the bar, he got into conversation with Willie Kinnell from Bowhill, who was demolishing a pie supper. Willie was as shy as Tam was, but the excited chat moved quickly from meat in general to the specifics, especially when Willie revealed that he worked in an abattoir. When Tam told him what he had learned about Hitler, the slaughterman's eyes dilated. In that moment the West Fife Anti-Vegetarian Liberation Front was born.

They decided to go underground. They communicated in code. Suspect politicians were targeted, and poison pen letters sent. The two men travelled to Edinburgh and, undetected, threw meatballs in the direction of Prince Charles's limousine outside the General Assembly of the Church of Scotland. They wrote anti-vegetarian pamphlets which were run off by a psychopath from Lumphinnans with a printing machine. They composed anti-vegetarian letters, using pseudonyms, for the press, travelling as far as Aberdeen and Dumfries to post them. Willie, the younger man by fifteen years, painted whitewash signs on the roads, before sprinting off into the darkness.

The organisation grew in range of activities and rhetoric if not in numbers. Tam's Council house home, the Front's headquarters, held piles of cuttings from the likes of *The Central Fife Times, The Dumfries and Galloway Standard, The West Highland Free Press* and *The Orcadian*. At a series of secret meetings at a pub at Jamphlars ("Quelle belle champ de fleurs!" Mary Queen of Scots had declared when passing through the area, which was now scarred by coal bings). Tam and Willie clarified the Front's international goals - thereafter coded by them as "The Jamphlars Declaration" - as the eventual elimination of all vegetarians in Europe and the destruction of all vegetarian food. Nothing less would do.

And yet, and yet, the Front was not making much headway, given the extent of the international vegetarian conspiracy. You could hardly open a newspaper without seeing yet another brazen vegetarian recipe. The campaign would have to become tougher. Warning the world from Lochgelly was not easy.

When his mother died, Tam was heartbroken, yet strangely self-assured. She had been his one true love, but he did not have time to grieve. The sense of depression which settled on him was linked in his mind to the Vegetarian Plot. There was much to be done, and too little time in which to do it.

95

A poisoned cauliflower was planted in Marks and Spencers' food department. The Front issued a coded message claiming responsibility, and warned of attacks on stores which stocked vegetarian goods. These stores were destroying the fibre of the British way of life, said the poorly printed press release. Stones were thrown through the windows of suspects. (Tam and Willie became experts at identifying vegetarians by the way they walked, or by the shape of their mouths.) Some meat abstainers found their car tyres mysteriously deflated in the morning.

Tam filled himself with more and more meat. He was preparing himself for the inevitable day of confrontation.

It came on twenty ninth January, nineteen hundred and eighty four. A notice appeared in the window of Munro's the Butchers in Lochgelly, which sent Tam's blood pressure spiralling out of control.

"VEGETARIAN HAGGIS FOR SALE" said the sign. Vegetarian haggis! In Lochgelly! In the very shop where Tam bought his supplies! It was an insolent all-out attack on Scottish identity. Vegetarians were "coming out" without public embarrassment: their arrogance knew no limits. Vegetarian haggis in Lochgelly's main street! It was as if it had been written in the Book of Revelation itself.

The hour had now come.

If Tam was nervous when he entered the shop at nine a.m. he didn't show it. He had a pair of tights over his head, a reasonably good imitation plastic Rashkolnikov at the ready. There was only one customer in the shop, old Mrs McGurn.

"Everyvon lie on the floor," he commanded in what was intended as a foreign-sounding accent.

"Tam, I was sorry to hear about yer mither," said Mrs McGurn, "she was sich a nice soul."

Tam's eyes welled with tears, beneath the nylon.

96

"Tam, what have ye got this gear on for?" inquired Bill Sime, Munro's bluff manager.

Tam heard Willie's battered Marina estate revving up outside. There would be a diarrheal aroma in the car when he got in, he knew well.

"Put a' yer vegetarian haggises into this bag," he snarled at Bill, his voice muffled by the tights.

"Sure," said Bill, going into the back shop.

"Aye, she was a richt guid soul," wailed Mrs McGurn. Tam swallowed hard.

"Ah'm goin' tae destroy these haggises for the guid o' Scotland," Tam told Bill Sime, huskily.

"Sure," said the manager. "That'll be eighteen pounds, seventy five pence."

Tam rushed out of the shop, and the Marina roared off, swerving past the bin lorry. When the police car stopped them for speeding on the Cardenden road, Tam protested his innocence strongly.

"It wisnae me!" he cried, but it was less than convincing. He had forgotten to take the tights off his head.

Tam conducted his own defence at Dunfermline Sheriff Court. He did not contest the police evidence that there had been found under the floorboards of his house explosives from the old Bowhill Colliery, a diagram of the Fife Health Board headquarters, 55 pies and 131 bridies. When he was sentenced to nine months imprisonment, he merely said bitterly, and cryptically, "So Hitler has won the war."

It was not the court case which made Tam famous, but its aftermath. He refused all food. On one occasion, when lentil roast was put down in front of him, he stuck it in the warder's face. Tam's threat to fast to the death was not taken seriously - that is, until he died, face to the wall,

sooner than might have been expected. All he said was that he looked forward to seeing his mother again. The book on the table in his cell, from the prison library, was *Hitler - Memoirs of a Confidant*, edited by Henry Ashby Turner. It was open at page 222, with pencil marks round the quotation - "When I met him a week later in Nurenberg, it came to my attention that he ate no meat. Unfortunately I myself had ordered goulash. I noticed Hitler fighting off nausea as I put the meat on my plate, though I did not make the connection. Suddenly he rose and said: 'I'll sit over there. Please join me when you're finished.'"
Beside it Tam had scribbled "It is finished".

The town turned out for the funeral. So did the media. Pictures of Tam Pollock being buried beside his mother made the Six o'clock News. Tam would have been proud, taken seriously now.

The West Fife Anti-Vegetarian Liberation Front at last got national attention. The local minister took the service awkwardly, not knowing whether to speak of the deceased as a criminal or a martyr. When he finished with "Till We Meet at Jesus' Feet", no one thought it funny. Bill Sime and Joe McGurn were among the cordbearers. Two hundred mourners sat down to steak pie and peas in the Station Hotel. No vegetarian option.

No one speaks of it now. No one even thinks of it. Except Willie Kinnell. Unemployed since the abattoir closed, he goes every week alone to Lochgelly cemetery to drink a can of lager and eat a bridie at Willie's grave: and remembers, and waits.

Fathers and Brethren

The almost Right Reverend Jonathan D. Smith, MA, BD, DD, smiled to himself as he stood outside the Assembly door. He touched with reverence the pristine, white lace which ran down the front of his preaching gown; freshly laundered, it had belonged to one of his great heroes, the Very Reverend Dr Alexander White. He knew that inside the Assembly Hall, the fathers and brethren were going through the opening formalities which would culminate in the announcement of his name. He would then stride confidently down the aisle to be received by the outgoing Moderator, and the coveted ring would be slipped onto his finger.

As he stood there, waiting, he turned to his senior chaplain and long-time friend, the Reverend Alex Buchan. "You've even combed your hair, Alex!" Jonathan joshed goodnaturedly. "This must be a big occasion! Watch carefully what happens here, my boy, for it'll be your turn, soon!"

"Your wish is my command, Your Holiness," replied Alex, doing a mock bow in the direction of the big, rotund man with the gaiters and silver buckled shoes.

The Moderator-Elect had rehearsed the scene so often in his imagination – not just in the six months since the Committee to Nominate the Moderator had announced his name, but for years beforehand: in fact, since he had gone to his first charge in rural Perthshire. Or was it when he was a theological student at New College in Edinburgh?

Yes, perhaps it was. Yes, definitely. He remembered it now: he used to walk past the outstretched arm of the cold-eyed Knox and on up the stairs to the lecture rooms, dreaming about what it would be like to wear the lace as part of the solemn procession of Lord High Commissioner, divines, and law lords.

He regularly played the home-made movie in his head: the green, hard benches of the Assembly Hall: the fourteen hundred men from the isles, rural areas, towns and cities of Scotland: the packed, excited public benches: the ladies, with their big hats, smiling in the Moderator's gallery: and himself in the Moderator's chair, presiding proudly over the nearest thing to Scotland's own parliament.

In his secret heart, he knew that he deserved the honour (though, of course, there were no circumstances in which he would utter that thought aloud). As a matter of self-honesty, he was prepared to acknowledge to himself that had served the Church of Scotland with distinction. Three parishes. Convener of the Kirk's Committee on Moral Welfare. Made a Doctor of Divinity by Edinburgh University. And now, at the age of 64, he was ready for the ultimate, crowning challenge.

He had already honed and repeatedly rehearsed his keynote message - a rousing and inspiring call in support of traditional family life, especially in the face of the subversive, permissive ideas coming from America.

During his time at Moral Welfare, he had been a vigorous opponent of all those he saw as enemies of the family - especially feckless single parents, homosexuals (why did the newspapers persist in adopting the fashionable American misnomer "gay"?) and the increasingly vocal feminists. It was not that he had anything against women, but he believed, with Saint Paul, that the man should be head of the household, as Christ was the head of the Church.

He was proud of the fact that as convener of the Committee on Moral Welfare, he had helped devise the "Family Fanfare" programme, with its ringing declarations in support of family life being read from every pulpit in the land. In the report to be submitted to the General Assembly, he had written, "We are encouraged by Her Majesty the Queen's forthright declaration on the occasion of her Silver Wedding celebrations with regard to family life, 'I am for it!' "

Yes, Jonathan felt he could lead a movement which would reverse the current trends. He was concerned that membership of the Kirk had dropped to 1,100,187, but he was exasperated by the dismal prophets who kept saying that it would fall even further. He was sure that with vigorous leadership, the number of signed-up members would not drop to below the one million mark; indeed, he was confident that the membership graph would take an upward turn....

He touched the lace again. His father would have been proud of him today. He had been a kirk elder and freemason, a hardworking man, a cabinet maker. A strong disciplinarian, Howard Smith occasionally beat his children, but only for their own good. He had worked extra hours to ensure that his only son could attend Edinburgh Academy. His earnings, even with overtime, could not pay for fees for all his children; his two daughters attended the local high school, but he had been glad to note that they did not seem at all envious of their brother. Jonathan sighed as he thought of his father. He still missed him, dead so young; especially on this special day....

Jonathan had been amazed at how his widowed mother had not only coped, but flourished, though in idiosyncratic ways. Bewilderingly, she had begun to dress more frivolously, and had started to travel for the first time in her life. She had even taken to wearing lipstick! She would be in the Moderator's gallery with her daughter Alice – seated not far from the Lord High Commissioner – looking grand in the wide-brimmed hat, specially bought for the occasion. His wife and loyal supporter, Jean, would be there too, with Miriam and David and their children, allowed off school for the occasion. Yes, he mused, the family would be proud of him.

His mind drifted to another sadness. One person who would not be there was his other sister, Gillian. They had not spoken for some years. The rift had begun when she had left her husband and gone to the United States. Jonathan had been furious with her, and told her so. Gill was now behaving like a middle-aged hippy, involving herself in demonstrations against the Vietnam war.

What was worse was that her own daughters supported her in her folly. Jonathan had only heard from her directly once since then; she had communicated with him after one of his speeches – condemning divorce, and the fashionable new 'hot pants' and mini-skirts - had not only made headlines in the Scottish popular press, but had, inexplicably, been reported in the *San Francisco Gazette*. "John," she had written in her familiar spidery hand, "with your unreasoning attacks on vulnerable people who already feel guilty enough, you are endangering your own soul."

Enraged by this insouciance, he had not replied. Through the frosted glass in the door of Assembly hall, Dr Smith saw the figure of the Assembly officer coming towards him. Time to go in to be acclaimed by the fathers and brethren. He fingered the lace again, straightening it. "Don't let me down now, Alex, or you'll never sit in that chair," he said to his chaplain, with a smile.

The officer, who would precede him slowly down the aisle, moved towards Jonathan. Charlie's face was normally solemn on such occasions, but it was even more grave than usual.

"Cheer up, man," said the grinning Moderator-Elect. "This isn't a funeral, you know!"

"I'm afraid there's been a hold up, sir, an objection, and it may take some time," the officer said apologetically. "I'm instructed to suggest that you retire to the Moderator's room until the matter is resolved."

What could possibly be the matter?

Alex Buchan was concerned. "Will I come in with you, and make you a cup of tea?" he asked anxiously.

"No, for God's sake, I need to be alone," the Moderator-Elect snapped at his friend.

"I'll be right outside if you need anything, Jonathan. I'm sure that whatever has come up, it won't take long to sort out."

The retiring room door slammed shut. He needed to be on his own, to clear his head. The sweat was cold on his forehead, and he felt faint. What had gone wrong? The election of a Moderator was a formal matter. Who could possibly object to him, Dr Jonathan D. Smith?

At the very moment of asking the question, a face came to mind. Sandy Turnbull! Surely not. His great rival for the convenership of the Committee on Moral Welfare would not have been so petty as to oppose his nomination on the floor of the General Assembly? Jonathan flushed as he recalled the circumstances of his victory over Turnbull. "I shouldn't have lobbied against him," he groaned to himself, head in hands. "Why did I do it?"

He had been desperate to get the nomination. Turnbull had looked as if he might be inching ahead, so Jonathan had let it be known over sherry at the New Club that his

104

rival had once had to have psychiatric treatment after overworking in his difficult parish. The insinuated doubts had probably tipped the balance.

So was this Turnbull's revenge? He pictured his adversary pleading with the fathers and brethren with weasel words of sympathy, while enjoying plunging the knife in, time and again.

"Bastard!" he shouted in the Moderator's room. Then remembered that he could be heard out in the main corridor. "Bastard!" he whispered plaintively.

Or had another of his rivals found out that he had not actually gained a First Class Honours degree from New College? It could have been Ramsay, who had always been jealous of him at college, and been beaten by him for the presidency of the Divinity Students Council. Sure, he had tweaked his CV a little when he had applied for the Cathedral; after all, he had gained a two-one, and had deserved a First. It was only because he had a cold on the day of the exam that he hadn't done quite so well as he had expected. It was hardly a major crime, was it? Surely not enough to deprive him of the Moderatorship?

Ramsay would also know that his proper name wasn't Jonathan. And that he didn't actually have a middle name. Plain John Smith. Too plain, in fact. That is why he had started calling himself Jonathan D. Smith. It sounded more….dignified, substantial. The Reverend Jonathan D. Smith, MA, BD, looked so much better on the church noticeboards and the headed notepaper. When he was awarded his honorary Doctorate of Divinity, he used to roll the words around on his tongue, the Reverend Doctor Jonathan D. Smith.….

Now, all he could hear was Ramsay addressing the Assembly, in that affected, self-important way of his: "Moderator, fathers and brethren, much as I hate to cause

105

offence, conscience dictates that I draw your attention to some matters which must militate against allowing Dr Smith to occupy the Moderator's chair, one which has been occupied by so many distinguished men of God. If I were to refrain from speaking out now, I would be arraigned before the judgment seat of God to answer for my cowardly silence."

Dr Smith groaned. Had it all come to this? His hands were trembling. Had he taken his blood pressure pill this morning, amidst all the excitement? He wanted to scream. The words of the Psalmist came into his mind: *Thou preparest a table before me in the presence of mine enemies.* The enemies were all around him, but where was the table? Where was the anointing of oil? Where was the cup that runneth over? Where was the God he had so loyally served all these years?

His mind was out of control. This could not get much worse.

Suddenly, unbidden, there came an image which he had forcibly put in a mental hole into the ground and covered up with earth, years ago. Oh, no... surely not that! Edinburgh Academy.

All these years ago. Age 15. He and Alex McArthur, a boy in the year above him. It had been a short-lived infatuation, but some of the other boys at the school had heard about it, and had given him a hard time. 'Poof!', 'Jessie!', 'Nancy boy!' they had called after him. He had felt utterly miserable, almost suicidal, even though he had gone on to win the Academical Club prize for classics. The school prize-giving ceremony – with its perpetual talk of old boys such as Robert Louis Stevenson and Archbishop Tait, and the sounds of *Floreat Academia* and the traditional cheers – had been painful. His beaming parents in the gallery had had no inkling of the inward distress of their outwardly confident son.

106

Had one of his enemies been tipped off about his indiscretion? There could be no greater public humiliation. In the light of the accusation, the stern-faced fathers and brethren would not allow him to become Moderator. He had observed of late that a new cynicism had entered the reporting of Kirk matters – not even *The Scotsman* could be relied on any more – and the representatives of the gutter press would record every detail, with relish. He could see the billboards in the Edinburgh streets: "Kirk chief in Gay Sex Scandal".

In that room, used by so many fine men of the Kirk in the past, the feelings of inadequacy and burning shame he had experienced as a teenager came flooding over him. He felt chilled. He was ruined.

What would Jean think as she sat in the gallery, hearing these embarrassing accusations? He could see her: face slightly tense, drawn, biting her lip, a little fear in the eyes. For years now, he had sensed a kind of defeat, of resignation about her.

When he had first met Jean – at the Youth Fellowship of the Canongate Kirk, where Dr Ronnie Selby Wright, another of his heroes, was minister – she struck him as a generous, outgoing girl. She was a student nurse, he an Arts student at Edinburgh University. Following his irregular Academy experiences, he was keen for some reassuring sexual experimentation. There was a problem, though: Jehovah was particularly offended by pre-marital sex. The Christian code did not sanction too much intimacy; even holding hands was described as "dangerous". So he was overcome by remorse when, after much pleading on his part, the terrible deed was done, in haste. It was the first time for both. That night, when he got back to his room in the student residence, he was in a panic. He struck a deal.

"Lord, if Jean doesn't become pregnant," he prayed fervently, "I'll become a minister."

It was an offer which the Lord couldn't refuse, apparently. And John Smith was a man of his word. New College it was.

In his first charge, he was zealous and idealistic. He worked night and day, always available to the parish. Jean was a model minister's wife, forever baking and knitting and smiling, even when some particularly vicious member of the Woman's Guild criticised her husband unjustly. She knew how hard John worked - in fact, she hardly saw him. When his father had died in his second year in the parish, John had hardly broken stride. He declined to talk about it, even when Jean questioned him gently.

He had become very excited when Jean became pregnant. He wanted a son, to be called Howard. It turned out to be a very difficult birth, one which meant that they could have no more children. Little Miriam had a lot of illness, up a lot at night, and Jean had become worn down. Her husband became even more remote, especially as his dreams for the parish foundered on the obduracy of his kirk session. He wanted out. He wanted a different kind of ministry, one that would bring him more satisfaction. He wanted to be near to the Kirk's headquarters at 121 George Street in Edinburgh.

It was when he applied for Duddingston parish church that he became the Reverend Jonathan D. Smith. His wife learned about the name change - and his desire to leave his parish - when she found a copy of his application as she dusted the study. She looked at him with pain in her eyes over the breakfast table. He offered no coherent explanations.

His mother was amused. "Jonathan! Well I never! I never thought I'd have a son called Jonathan," she chuckled. "And what, may I ask, does the D stand for? Dumpling?"

Jonathan D was in pain. He was cold, and hot, and palpitating. He hated everybody, not least himself. A wave of nausea washed over him. He rushed to the toilet, and vomited into the lavatory pan. He noticed a dark red colour amidst the vomit.

Blood. Had it come to this? *Though your sins be scarlet, saith the Lord, they shall be white as snow.* For some strange reason, the sight of the blood took him back to his days as a child, attending Band of Hope meetings with a friend. He remembered a hymn they used to sing to the tune of *Auld Lang Syne*. The words - made even more grotesque by the melody - flooded into his mind, and he began to mouth them, weeping involuntarily.

There is a fountain filled with blood
Drawn from Immanuel's veins;
And sinners plunged beneath that flood,
Lose all their guilty stains.
Lose all their guilty stains, my Lord
Lose all their guilty stains!
And sinners plunged beneath that flood,
Lose all their guilty stains....

Then, overwhelmed, the never-to-be-Right Reverend Jonathan D. Smith slumped forward in his seat.

Alex Buchan pounded again on the door. Why was he not answering? Had he fallen asleep? What was wrong? Had he had a heart attack? A stroke?

Alex tried the door, but it was locked from the inside. He must get help quickly. He ran along the black and white corridor, puffing, and reached the medical room. "Quick," he shouted breathlessly, "I think there's something wrong with the Moderator. He's in the retiring room, and I can't get an answer. The door's locked."

Alex ran back along the corridor, with two medical assistants bringing up the rear, equipment in hand. He pounded on the door again. Suddenly, thankfully, the handle moved, and the door opened, slowly. Jonathan appeared, looking dazed, eyes slightly reddened.

"Jonathan, thank God you're safe. I was really worried when you didn't answer."

"Have you been banging long?" asked Jonathan, looking bewilderedly at the two men in white coats.

"Jonathan," said Alex. "It is finished....."

"I know, I know," Jonathan said resignedly.

"It was all a fuss about nothing. Apparently Robert Thomson objected that the proper procedures hadn't been followed by the Committee to Nominate the Moderator. He said he'd nothing against you personally, in fact he thought you were a first class candidate, but it was a matter of principle that he challenge the nomination."

"Do you need us, sir?" asked one of the medical assistants. "Are you all right?"

"There's nothing the matter with me," replied Jonathan, wiping the sweat off his brow. He could hardly take in what he was hearing. "Did no one object to me? Sandy Turnbull? Tom Ramsay?"

"No, no. Why on earth should they?" It was the chaplain's turn to be bewildered. He went on, "I gather that the convener had to make a statement, and the commissioners questioned him. He eventually conceded that there had been some minor irregularities in the procedures. The Assembly rebuked him, but they voted to install you regardless. So now you're definitely onstage! What do you say to that, Moderator!"

Jonathan looked at his friend, and said, without a smile, "I have been saved."

Thou hast prepared a table before me in the presence of mine enemies. Thou anointest my head with oil. My cup runneth over. "I have been saved," he said again. "The table is set."

The late John Smith, now the almost Right Reverend Jonathan D. Smith, breathed deeply as he stood outside the Assembly Hall door, waiting for his cue. He touched the white lace. His legs still felt shaky, but he was beginning to recover his equilibrium. It was as if what had happened had been a bad dream, not unlike some of the miserable dreams that had haunted him for most of his life. Now, he could see clearly the purpose of these night-time visitations: they had been sent to test his faith. Like Job, he had come through. These experiences would make him a better leader.

Through the frosted glass, he saw the Assembly officer approach. Charlie permitted himself a glimmer of a smile. "I don't want any more jokes about funerals, sir," he said.

The outgoing Moderator, Dr James Bremner, was an old friend.

"Jonathan," he said warmly, "On behalf of the Assembly, I apologise to you for the delay. Knowing you, I'm sure that you enjoyed the unscheduled time of conversation with the Lord before the start of Assembly business. You would have blushed if you had heard the things that were said about you in your absence. I concur with the sentiments. You will make a fine leader for our beloved Kirk."

Loud applause rolled around the green benches and the public gallery as the Moderatorial ring was placed on the appropriate finger. A hush fell upon the Assembly as the Right Reverend gentleman prepared to address the commissioners.

"Moderator......sorry, I *am* the Moderator...."

The huge hall convulsed with laughter. Exactly the response he had imagined, as he had rehearsed it, so often.

"Fathers and brethren, it is my privilege to stand before you this morning as your new Moderator. I am truly humbled to receive this unexpected honour."

"Humbled! Unexpected!" his mother chortled under her wide-brimmed hat. "Well I never!"

The Moderator glanced up to the gallery, and saw a look of pain on his wife's face.

"These are difficult days for the Church, especially when the family is under sustained attack from all sides. I am proud to be chosen to lead the counter attack."

The applause was loud and long. As he looked with appreciation around the hall, he noticed a woman, dressed in something resembling a sari, standing up in the middle of the public gallery, opposite the Moderator's chair. She simply stood there, a disturbing presence, looking at him. She seemed vaguely familiar, though he couldn't quite place her. It was only when she turned silently and deliberately and walked out of the door that he realised who she was.

Gillian. His sister. Gill.

He carried on. "There is a fountain….I mean a mountain, to climb, but with God, nothing is impossible."

More ringing applause. It was as he had visualised it. God was good. Yes, the table had been set.

The Right Reverend Doctor Jonathan D. Smith, MA, BD, DD, ran his fingers down the lace. It was reassuringly pure, and perfect, and white, apart from a small spot of vomit, flecked with blood.

The Christmas illumination of Sir Geeza Bung

Sir George Bung felt pleased with himself as he rolled the cigar round his lips. More than pleased with himself, in fact. Delighted. Yes, delighted. The Lord, or whoever was In Charge, had done him proud.

The sound of carollers outside in the snow swelled his already surging good humour. *Once in Royal David's City*, his favourite. He bounded benevolently to the door and gave the singers ten pounds with a cheery greeting.

Not many Bridgeton scrap merchants had risen to own a bungalow in Newton Mearns, never mind own shares in BT, never mind hold Glasgow's highest office, never mind be knighted! Arise, Sir George! Yes, he had done well, even if he said it himself, which he did, often.

Because this was a special night, and because he would be on duty soon, he had put on his shining chain of office. As he sat in his favourite chair, at his own fireside, wearing the badge of such high rank, he felt an inner glow. He swallowed another Highland Park and looked across the fireside at his beloved helpmeet, the Lady Agnes. As always, she was knitting.

"Agnes..." he said, the voice full of benign intention.

"For God's sake, Dod," she interrupted, "Aggie."

"Aggie" pained him. As did "Dod". Dod Bung did not

sound a name to be reckoned with. More like a kind of cheap glue.

He had been nicknamed "Geeza" early on. After he became convener of the Planning Committee, the name proved to be a continual embarrassment. Geeza Bung. The best Cooncillor money can buy, and so on. And on.

"Aggie," he said, now with a slightly irritable edge to the benevolence, "It'll soon be time for the carols in George Square. When is the car coming?"

"Hauf past ten" replied Lady Aggie Bung, without looking up.

"I love Christmas Eve," mused Geeza, expansively, pouring himself another 12-year-old single malt. "Nothing can spoil its innocence."

Within ten minutes, the fuse had been well and truly lit.

"Dod, whit are we gonny dae aboot Maria?" Aggie said suddenly, concentratedly.

Geeza spilt his whisky. The name hit him like a pailful of cold water. Maria. What was he going to do about Maria?

"Surely when it's Christmas...." trailed Aggie, plaintively.

"Christ!" exploded Sir George. "Geeza brek, wull ye, Aggie! It's Christmas, the season o' fuckin' goodwill! An' you're talkin' aboot Maria!"

Christmas Past. Christmas Present. Christmas Spoiled.

Geeza's breathing was quick and harsh. The cigar was out.

The tense silence was broken only by the clicking of Lady Aggie's needles. Bootees.

He had wanted good things for his daughter, better things than he had had. He had sent her to the best school. He had wanted her to go to University and become

114

a smart lawyer, but she had wasted her time, got in with the wrong crowd. Despite the hard-earned money he had spent, her glottal stop remained. No: that was too neutral a description. She had *retained* her glottal stop. Even exaggerated it. It was the most expensive glottal stop in Glasgow. Not only that, she dared to mock her father's painfully adopted pan-loaf accent, especially when, stretching to his full, rotund, five foot four inches, he spectacularly lost his temper – as he often did – and the torrents of east-end vernacular came pouring through the inadequately shored-up west-end dam. When that happened, Maria danced exultantly, screaming with laughter, tears rolling down her cheeks, imitating her father maniacally.

He had wanted her to have a white wedding in the chapel. He often pictured the scene in his mind....tails and top hat, Lady Agnes in nice, obviously expensive dress, the photographs....Instead, Maria was living defiantly in a Council flat in Possil with a Protestant layabout called Jimmy.

The embarrassment Maria caused him was painful. He had been able to cope with her wildness until it became public knowledge. She made headlines when she demonstrated on the streets against the Glasgow Councillors, her father included, for their "crimes against the people". She was picked up by the police several times for breach of the peace at demonstrations in George Square. She had become so familiar with the inside of police vehicles that the press dubbed her "Black Maria". She issued statements condemning what she called "the Fascist Militia of George Square". The Lord Provost was not amused.

Sir George had done a lot to improve the image of Glasgow, working closely with a public relations firm which had coined the slogan "I'm Glasgowing to the City of Dreams". He regularly attacked Glaswegian writers for producing novels full of swear words - books which, although he had not read them, showed the city, he said, in a bad light. What rage, then, when he saw the photographs on the front page of the *Record* – the squalid tenement in Possil, with Maria and Jimmy and the others holding up a banner declaiming "We're Wallowing in the City of Nitemares". And when the *Sun* had got hold of the story of Maria's pregnancy they had announced the news, with typical crudity, in front-page banner headlines A BUNG IN THE OVEN! Alongside the proudly swollen Maria, they had placed a photo of her father in full civic regalia.

It was not just the tabloids. The quality press had tormented him too. Even the *Herald*. Jack Maclean had revelled in the righteous Lord Provost's discomfiture, describing Sir George as "that jumped-up wee Brigton nyaff with a lavvy chain round his neck". John Macleod had slain him in a flood of awesome Gothic-Old Testament rhetoric. Brian Meek, in a column headed "Geeza Gift from God", had exulted that a Bung had filled the hole in the dyke that stood between the Scottish Tories and oblivion.

And the baby was due at Christmas.

Whit are we gonny dae aboot Maria? Another Highland Park.

Not all of his family had turned bad. The youngest boy, Gonville, the only one to be born in Newton Mearns, had followed his father into local politics. He was now convener of Planning, nicknamed inevitably "Gonny Geeza Bung". The oldest boy, Francis, had made his mark and wealth in some mysterious business in the south of England, something to do with lobbying MPs, and was married to an English property agent. He only managed to get home once a year, at New Year time, earning himself the soubriquet "Black Bung" in Tom Shields's scurrilous

116

Diary in the *Herald*. The twins, Timothy and Nicholas, were both in insurance. They had married nice girls and lived in bungalows in Bonkle.

But Maria: she was something else. Whit are we gonny dae aboot Maria? The searing phrase ran amok in his maddened brain like an insistent refrain from the *Sound of Music*. Manic Glaswegian nuns came running down the Austrian hillsides of his fevered mind, singing "Whit are we gonny dae aboot Maria?" A treble whisky, poured with shaky arm.

Sir George adjusted his chain as he settled into the back seat of the civic Daimler beside Lady Bung. His face was flushed. A whisky bottle was on the seat beside him.

"Take me to twenty Clarence Court in Possil," he instructed the chauffeur.

"Not to George Square, sir?" asked the suprised driver.

"Do as I say," replied Sir Geeza, in commanding tone.

Aggie was dumfounded, but pleased. She knew her husband well enough not to display her pleasure. He was in resolute man-of-action mode, and it thrilled her. She did not even protest when he swigged straight from the Highland Park bottle.

The gleaming car, its windscreen wipers rhythmically swishing aside the snowflakes, made its way past houses with boarded-up windows. The graffiti shouted foul messages from the walls. The despair was tangible.

The City of Dreams.

Clarence Court used to be called Nitshill Road, but had been renamed as part of the "positive thinking" exercise introduced by the city's image-makers. If you think you are in a classy street, you will become classy yourself, they had told the sullen tenants.

Number Twenty.

"Keep the engine running," Sir Geeza instructed the

117

driver. Curious children swarmed around the Daimler, putting their sticky fingers on the shining bonnet. The couple went into the closemouth.

It was the stench of stale urine which stopped Sir George Bung in his jelly-legged tracks and transformed Christmas for him for ever.

It wafted him straight back to his childhood, more than sixty years ago. Passing through his nostrils, it seared his befuddled brain, and recovered in an instant that sense of unremitting poverty which had disfigured his youth. Long-dormant anger flared up in him again. The pungent smell suddenly reminded him of why he had gone into politics in the first place.

Where had he been all his life?

He paused, inhaled the life-changing fumes deep into his lungs, then bounded up the stairs, two at a time, to the top flat.

"Whit do you want," said a dishevelled Jimmy, as he opened the door.

"We've come tae see Maria," said Geeza. "It's Christmas."

"Ah know it's fuckin' Christmas," said Jimmy. "Have ye left yer reindeer ootside. Wid ye no rather come doon the fuckin' lum?"

Sir Geeza pushed his way past. Jimmy was surprised.

"She's in there," he pointed. "She's jist had a wee boy."

Sir Geeza barged straight into the room, Lady Aggie close behind him.

Maria was in bed, tiny child on her bosom. The midwife was by the bed.

Maria wept. "Ah wantit ye tae come, but Ah didnae want tae ask ye."

Dod and Aggie embraced her.

"Ah've no been very well," said Maria. "Ah want ye tae help me wi' the wean for the next while, ma. Jimmy'll never

118

cope."

"Whit's his name?" asked Geeza.

"George," she replied. "....at least that's what Ah'm gonny call him."

"But....Ah thought ye hated me."

"Ah did. Ah still do, maist o' the time. But since Ah've been no well, Ah've been thinkin'. Ah couldna get through tae ye, but maybe a bairn wi' your name can. Maybe ye can gie up a' this pompous garbage. Maybe ye can still dae something, for his nibs here, if for naebody else."

"Are ye gonny get wee Dod christened?" he asked, tenderly.

"Naw," she said. "What's religion ever done for us? Catholics and Prodisants, arguin' wi' each other. Priests an' ministers gettin' money oot o' us. Ah'd rather he wis a human being."

"But...." His blood started to rise, instinctively.

"Quiet, Dod" interrupted Aggie, authoritatively, producing the bootees, and laying them beside the baby. George had brought nothing for the child, but he knew instinctively what to do. He took off his gold chain of office, and gently laid it in a circle around the baby, around the breast. He kissed the child, breathing whisky fumes over him. Things which had been confused had now become clear, momentarily at least, in the spirit. He'd rather he was a human being - in the meantime, anyway, on this night of sparkling clarity. Tomorrow was another day.

"Ah think he's a right wee cracker," said Geeza, exultantly. "Ah'm prood o' you, hen."

Maria smiled, tearfully, exhausted.

Outside, revellers from a party bawled, almost in drunken parody, *Once in Royal David's City.*

City of dreams.

In the street, the gleaming engine of state was still purring.

It could wait.

A day in the death of a minister

I
t was 20th May, 2009, three years after the Church of
England was privatised. (The Church of Scotland had
been dealt with the year before.) And an eerie mist
covered the land.

Sandy knew the details of the church controversies
well. In fact, he was writing his own definitive history of
them. He had studied the stories often enough in the
library, going over the material time and again. It was how
he passed his days, scribbling notes in his thin, italic
writing. These things needed to be chronicled, even though
few people were interested in such matters now. Here is
what he had written down for posterity in his spiral-bound
notebook:

*The facts. The government had decided that the time had
come to take on the Church of England, "the last bastion of
protected state privilege". (Actually, that's not quite true. The
greatest remaining state monopoly was the monarchy. When
the rumours of a royal abdication were at their height, a
secret paper had been presented to the cabinet, suggesting
that the royal state monopoly should be broken up, and the
monarchy itself put out to tender. Sealed bids would be
invited. What a storm there was when the paper was leaked!
It argued that it was illogical to exempt the monarchy and
church from the changes which had "brought fresh air
sweeping through every other national institution". It was*

time, it said, to let the same hurricane blow through even the so-called sacrosanct institutions. Oh to have been a fly on the wall in the cabinet room when the Queen did eventually abdicate! Apparently some ministers came to blows on the question of whether foreigners, blacks and homosexuals should be excluded from the bidding. No mention of disabled people: should they have been angry?)

So the denomination which used to be known as the "Church of England" lost its protected status and privileges, and became The Episcopal Church (England). When Charles and Camilla succeeded to the throne, the rights and privileges of being the national church of England for ten years were put out to tender. The package not only included handling the Coronation service itself, but also the transport and catering franchises, as well as the television rights. The Mormon Church (England) with huge funds from America, and with powerful backing from omnipresent BSkyB Television and the Murdoch press, won the glittering prize. (The poor old Roman Catholic Church came second! It hadn't seemed so long ago since the Catholic Church had announced triumphally that it was in position to take over the role of England's national church. The Church of England had been at its weakest point, and some prominent royal defections had created the impression that all roads were leading to Rome. Then the "caretaker" Pope John XXIV caused mayhem with his revelation from heaven in the middle of the night - women could be ordained as priests! What fun! The Anglican clergy who had joined Rome because their own church had decided to ordain women in 1993 were beside themselves - couldn't have happened to nicer people. They were faced with a choice of joining the Free Kirk or the breakaway True Catholic Church, which took a lot of priests - and money - with it.)

A year earlier, the Church of Scotland had become The

Presbyterian Church (Scotland). Its national status had been easier to disentangle, because there were fewer constitutional implications. There had been few protests of any significance. (The liberals in the church had been routed in the post-millennial evangelical revival. The Kirk's conservatives had seized the initiative, especially those who had adopted the fashionable American "Evangelical Power" strategy - Evangelical Power breakfasts at Crieff, Evangelical Power Dressing! Evangelical Power Spectacles! They favoured a complete withdrawal from public issues and a concentration on private and personal spiritual power. They were indifferent to, and sometimes even hostile to, the Scottish parliament.)

Management consultants were brought in to look at the "Kirk" (as it was still sentimentally known), and far-reaching changes were made. Looking at the strengths and weaknesses of the 150,000-strong body, the consultants identified three main market sectors - baptisms, weddings and funerals - in which The Presbyterian Church (Scotland) could go for growth. Accordingly, the church had been broken up into three separate self-contained divisions, under the overall direction of a Chief Executive. In order to regain its share of the market and compete effectively for the main franchises, the former Church of Scotland's old headquarters at 121 George Street, Edinburgh had been sold to Marks & Spencers, and custom-built premises erected at an industrial estate in Livingston. The sale of the Assembly Hall on the Mound raised a substantial sum, which was used to fund the appointment of Regional Growth Directors.

As part of the drive to make the Presbyterian Church "leaner and fitter", all remaining "non -viable" units were closed, and at least one "Major Worship Centre" was

123

designated for each Region. Ministers (called
"clergypersons", a hangover from an EC directive made
before Britain left the Community in 2005 following John
Redwood's stunning victory over Gordon Brown) were
appointed to churches on three-year contracts, renewable
annually at the discretion of the Regional Growth
Directors. Each of the church's 150 pastors negotiated their
own salary and conditions, but their pay was
performance-related. As part of the package, every
clergyperson was given an annual recruitment target and
undertook to do two weeks management training every
year.

The consultants also decided, after extensive market
research, that the church's image was too gloomy and
negative. A new logo was designed with the slogan "Smile
with Jesus!", accompanied by a Mr Happy figure.
Following a slick television advertising campaign
(designed by advisers from the rapidly growing American
Southern Baptist Church and funded by the Murdoch
press), there was an immediate financial turnaround in the
first year. (Why not sponsorship now? Why not the Hovis
Communion?) The slimmed-down, more upbeat kirk had
the confidence to look at smaller denominations with a
view to take-over and expansion as part of its new Growth
Strategy. It was rumoured that a bid was being prepared at
the Livingston HQ for the assets of the ailing rumps of the
Congregational Union (Scotland) and the Methodist
Church (Scotland).

Can one imagine Mr Happy being crucified? On
second thoughts, yes.

As he reviewed his notes in his notebook, Sandy
sighed and wrote with a wry smile, "It is finished".
He did not feel too much like Smiling with Jesus.
There was no longer a regular bus service to his town, and

no trains had run there for years. A car was necessary, but he could not afford one – not with petrol at £20 a gallon and £1000 a year road tax. It was all right for people in work with their high salaries and only 12 pence in the pound income tax – a guaranteed election winner for Mr Redwood – but the means-tested pension left nothing over once the huge heating bills had been paid. All these years on the minimum stipend had left him poorly off.

He had become a minister in 1959. He had a vocation then. He sighed now when he recalled his zeal as a young man, leading crusades on behalf of his people against dampness in the high-rise flats, and against the money-lenders who preyed upon the poorest in the community. He was bold then, angry about injustice. Supported by his wife, Agnes, who had Parkinson's disease – "Agnes Dei" he used to call her, affectionately; their chief regret was that they had no children – he had led his congregation into the community. The long hours and continual availability had exhausted him, as had the intractability of the never-einding problems facing him.

After 20 years in that first parish, he came close to breakdown. The rest of his ministry was spent in a linked country parish, working hard, caring for the people, building bridges between the church and the community, trying in vain to halt the decline in church membership.

What had troubled him more deeply, though, was a much wider, more ominous corrosive gnawing. He had felt acutely the silent but inexorable disintegration of any sense of shared values. As a sensitive and caring man, he could feel within his being the turning of people away from each other, a retreat into private, individual concerns. The large numbers of unemployed, the homelessness and the growing drug dependency had given the country a very shadowy and ominous feel. Many people were wealthy, but most seemed to be under continual stress at work. Their

125

homes were not just their castles, but fortresses. It was as if people had become blinded, as if they were in a deep mist, under a spell, and did not even know the extent of their loss.

When he retired, he felt something of a failure. His ideals had not been realised. It was the death of Agnes, six years into the brash new millennium, that led Sandy into his deepest despair. He felt humiliated by the fact that he had not been able to afford proper medical care. The embarrassing questions at the hospital about his finances, the endless form-filling, the poverty of his health insurance arrangements, and the knowledge that health care for the likes of him was dependent on a national fund-raising lottery made Agnes's terminal illness all the harder to bear. His anger – the old anger that had once come out in his dealings with landlords and loan sharks – had suddenly erupted in the hospital.

"This is a fucking disgrace!" he had shouted, uncharacteristically, at the consultant. (He only swore on exceptional occasions.)

"I'm surprised at you, a minister," the consultant said, sadly.

After this, he had become a recluse, studying the details of obscure ecclesiastical debates in the local library, writing endlessly in his spiral-bound notebook. The *Scotsman* and the *Herald* had become regional Murdoch journals. Someone had to tell the truth.

He walked on through the town, past the old kirk. It had closed some two years previously. Non-viable. Most people could not afford to travel into the Major Worship Centre, though there was talk of a minibus coming out to pick up those without cars. Sandy used to go to the old kirk after he retired until the day, not long after Agnes's death, when the smart young minister, who came every second Sunday from a nearby town, played the Twenty Third Psalm on the guitar and insisted that the mainly geriatric congregation clap hands to the rhythm. He had introduced the "California Blessing" – which had succeeded and outdone the "Toronto Blessing" – and had invited the congregation to laugh hysterically with him under the influence of the Spirit – and even to bark (only if they wished). The old kirk was now a gleaming "Opportunity Centre" run by the burgeoning "Opportunity Knocks Enterprise".

His feet took him to the former Co-operative Society building. It was now the "Free Choice Centre", run by Human Choice plc. It gave advice on abortion and euthanasia (fees payable only at point of execution.) He found himself going in.

"Which service are you interested in, Mr Latimer?" asked the smart young man.

"Well, it's not likely to be abortion, is it?" said Sandy, without a flicker of expression.

The smart young man smiled wanly, but tolerantly. He had been on a training course on the subject of dealing with difficult clients.

"Euthanasia".

The smart young man gave him a glossy leaflet entitled "The Choice is Yours".

"Would you like the laser film that goes with it?" he asked, brightly.

"No. I don't even know what a laser film is."

"If you want to follow the matter through after you've read the literature, we'll provide a counsellor to take you through the options."

"Wonderful, Counsellor", said Sandy, again without a flicker of expression.

"What?" said the young man.

The old minister left the Free Choice Centre and shuffled towards the library. He wanted to read more about the history of the Free Kirk struggle. The Wee Free Choice Kirk! How about that for a name! He laughed aloud, till he was suddenly reminded that it was Assembly time for The Presbyterian Church (Scotland). The Assembly – which hardly rated a paragraph in the *Herald* and *Scotsman* – was a three-day event, over a long weekend in Livingston. It was advertised as a "caring and sharing festival", with Moody and Sankey hymns and modern choruses interspersing the inspirational talks by the Regional Growth Directors and the motivational seminars on time management. Mr Happy beamed above it all.

Although he had made fun of it at the time, Sandy thought with nostalgia of the solemn church-and-state ceremony of the General Assembly of the Church of Scotland on the Mound, and the intensity and passion of some of the debates. It all seemed so interesting now (even though he had often been bored at the time). He thought of the times when he and Agnes had attended the Assembly Garden Party at Holyrood Palace. The event seemed to be always sunny in his memory! He remembered the day when one senior minister of the Kirk, who, in a panic as he realised that his false teeth were stuck to a meringue as the Queen approached, threw meringue and teeth behind a bush and faced Her Majesty with flashing gums.

As he crossed the road, Sandy found himself laughing maniacally, so loudly that people turned round in the street.

The car came towards him at speed, swerving, skidding. Sandy swayed backwards into its path, and he ended up on the bonnet, carried along for about two hundred yards before he came crashing off on to the roadway.

The young driver, distressed, jumped out. Music roared
out of the open door. "Clap! Clap! Clap your hands! Jesus
our king is coming back!" A familiar Mr Happy logo was
on the back window of the car.

Crowds gathered round as Sandy lay on the road.

"It wisnae your fault, son," someone said to the driver,
putting a sympathetic hand on to his camel-hair car coat.
"That crazy auld bugger must have a death wish."

The driver moved his head down to the old man. Lying
there, Sandy looked vulnerable as a child.

"I'm a clergyperson," the young man said. "Is there
anything I can do?"

It was only then that Sandy recognised him as the
young minister who had played the guitar in his church. It
all came back. The Lord's my Shepherd. Clap, Clap.....

The old man's lips moved. The voice was faint. The
driver moved closer.

"Is there anything I can do?" the young man repeated
plaintively, anxiously.

"You can turn off that fucking music," whispered the
old man. (This was an exceptional occasion).

"Would you like me to say a prayer?" said the young
man, not hearing.

"Only if you promise not to bark."

The young minister took out his Bible, and read the
words of Jesus: 'You have not chosen me, I have chosen
you.'

"The Wee Free Choice Kirk! " uttered the old man,
grimacing.

"What?" said the young minister.

Clap! Clap! Clap your hands.....

"It is finished," groaned the old man, as the sirens
mercifully drowned out the sound of the chorus. "Agnes
Dei", he muttered, with a faint smile.

"What?" said the young minister.

"Poor demented bugger," said the man in the crowd.

130

Scotland, Scotland

Gary grinned to himself as he laced up his new boots. For Chrissake, hadn't he looked forward to this day all year?

He'd been brought up on the stories: of booze, and blood, of heads kicked in, of polis-baiting. Magic.

He stood up, ready to go.

"C'mon!" he shouted to Billy, who was preening himself in front of the mirror. "What the fuck are ye waitin' for? At this rate ye might make the game for Hampden next year!"

Billy smiled. "Ah've been there afore," straightening his broad tie, picking a piece of fluff from his lapel. "Keep the heid, son. Don't wet yersel."

Gary dribbled an imaginary ball. "Have ye passed yer fitness test, then? There's nothin wrang wi' you that plastic surgery widnae cure!"

"At least there's nae danger o' you gettin' brain surgery," said Billy, one last sideways glance in the mirror. "An' yer chances o' gettin' a bird are even less. Ye look a right bluddy scruff."

Tee shirt, denim jacket, tartan scarf, tammy, jeans. Nothin wrang wi' that. Just because Billy fancied his barra in a suit...

"Oot the fuck'n road, Prince," intoned Gary, aiming a playful kick at the alsatian barring his path to the door.

131

"Mind yer handbag, Billy!"

- "Ye can shoot aboot as good as Alan Ball," cried the elder brother. "Ma, we're for aff."

Mrs Duffy was silently present. Present in defeat, as always. No more surprises any more, not even disappointments.

"Stay oot o' trouble, mind."

Aye, Ma. Aye. Nae danger.

The street was alive. The chimes of the van boomed the theme tune from Doctor Zhivago. Twenty Embassy tipped, an' a bottle o' Irn Bru. Are ye gaun tae the gemme? Aye. Tell Derek Parlane tae stick in three past Clemence.

The taxi took them quickly out of the scheme, into the city centre. Gary moved to the edge of the seat when he heard the chants of "Scotland, Scotland" resounding through the city streets, full of blood-curdling optimism. A thrill ran through him, goosepimply. Scotland, Scotland.

Not that the feeling was new. After all, he'd sung "Bring on the English!" on the Hampden terraces only three nights previously, when Scotland had gubbed Ireland. Yet this spine-tingling feeling was different. He felt vibrant, alive. It wasn't just the thought of watching Scotland crush England, as he knew they would. That was part of it, of course, fuelled by the papers. The Best Scottish Side for Years.

No, it was more than that. It was more than football. Wembley was the name of an excitement which ran straight to his bowels. Thank God Billy, so cool, didn't know what was going on inside him.

Gary gulped down a pint of beer. That helped. The noise in the pub was at crescendo level. A Rangers bar of course. Stewart Kennedy was the greatest Scottish keeper since Jimmy Cowan - he would keep out the English bastards with one hand. Sandy Jardine was magic. Derek Parlane would get at least three. Derek Johnstone should

132

have been playing instead of Dalglish or MacDougall. Nae danger.

The more Gary drank, the more proud he felt to be a Prodisant. Another pint of heavy. His da had been a great Prodisant. Put on his best suit to go to Belfast for the Twelfth. Black Preceptory. His da glowed when he got letters beginning "Dear Sir Knight..." He missed his da. Especially tonight. His da had been all right. Gary hadn't liked it when he beat his ma, and once he'd punched his old man when he'd been really vicious to her. But when he'd died in hospital, yellow, Gary had cried. Billy was stronger.

"Time tae go!" Gary shouted to his brother, who was seated at the table with his girl friend. "We don't want tae miss the train."

"Plenty o' time, son," laughed Billy, leaning over to kiss his Helen, the giggler from Drumchapel. "Yer no actually playin' at Wembley, ye know."

Gary could hardly sit still, squashed in the compartment of the Wembley Special. He tried to lose himself in the songs. All We are Saying, is Give us a Goal. He drank the lager can dry. Ready when you are.

"Nazi bastards!" he chanted with the rest, waving two fingers at the uniformed squadrons. The police stared balefully at the departing carriages, having given up the struggle to check for tickets, glad at the leaving of another train filled with the flower of Scotland.

"Poofs! Wankers!" roared the choir. Beer cans flew out of the open window. Wembley was only a stone's throw away.

The rhythm of the train, the lights of the city, the sense of impending glory excited Gary, who'd never been out of Glasgow in his seventeen years.

"Mebbe Ah'll stay doon in London efter the gemme,"

he mused in the direction of Billy, who was dividing his attention between Helen and a hand of cards. "Ah'll get a joab."

"Aye, they're cryin' oot for heidbangers wi' nae qualifications. There's adverts in the papers every day. Eedjit Wantit. Three hundred pounds a week."

Gary laughed, painfully. He'd hated school, had dogged it often, no questions asked. He'd left as soon as he could, to do the same as his da – nothing. Billy had been lucky.

Gary joined in the singing, restless. "If you hate the Glasgow Celtic clap your hands..."

The carriage door burst open.

"Get these fuck'n bluenoses!"

Gary defended himself, instinctively. Arms flailed, cards and money scattering. Blinded by blood, he caught a boot in the face, fell. He lashed out like a wounded animal, not knowing it was Billy he was kicking.

"Polis!" someone shouted. In an instant the compartment was half empty. Gary hadn't even noticed the train had stopped.

"How did ye get that?" asked the sergeant, pointing to the blood pouring down Gary's face.

"Ah fell," said Gary.

"Well ye never fell hard enough. Next time make sure ye fuck'n kill yersel."

The carriage was less noisy, more drunk, as the train lurched off. Gary crashed into the wall of the toilet. He tried to wash off the blood, standing in urine and vomit.

"Fenian bastards," he muttered.

Deep into England: train running like a fury, keen to unload its troublesome burden: continual shuffling back and forward: fans walking all the way to Wembley.

Gary wished the journey was over.

The train shuddered to a standstill, punters falling,

beer spilling. Sorry son. Polis again. Somebody stabbed. Oh God.

It was hours before the train moved. "Flower of Scotland", slightly wilted, began again. Gary desperately wanted to sleep, to dull the pain in his head.

He'd only been dozing a short time, when a loud voice broke through the dream.

"You. Ah want you!" pointed the heavyweight swaying at the compartment door, shirt hanging out, zip undone. Gary, alert immediately, froze. Behind the muscleman stood more of the same. The person being demanded was Helen.

"What dae ye mean?" she asked. No giggling.

"You ken what ah mean."

He grabbed her and pulled her towards him, right out of the compartment. Gary dived out of the door after them.

He never got near. The punches that felled him left him dazed. A vicious boot reopened the cut, sending blood tumbling down his face, blinding him. He lay on the floor, pierced by Helen's scream, unable to get his body to function.

"Billy, Billy," she wailed despairingly.

Gary had no idea how long he'd lain there, but when he came to he was aware that the corridor and the doorway were empty. Helen was whimpering. Her face was bleeding, her blouse had no buttons left.

It was only when Gary took her back to the compartment that it dawned on him that Billy hadn't moved.

"What the fuck are you playing at?" he accused his brother.

Helen flopped down on her boyfriend's knee, weeping. Billy dragged her to her feet.

"Get away fae me," he shouted, pushing her. "Ye

136

nivver were any fuck'n good. Yer just a bluddy hoor."

Helen drew her nails across Billy's face, drawing blood, then rushed out of the compartment. Gary stumbled after her, but she was gone. He went to the toilet, and examined his swollen face in the mirror. Why was he crying? He lurched back and forward, seeing his own distorted image, again and again and again. The melancholy cries of "Scotland, Scotland" sounded like the bleating of a pack of wounded animals.

He retched and vomited several times on the toilet floor.

Euston. The crowds poured out of the train, chanting and cheering, filled with new energy. A wave of tartan swept up to the gates, and charged them. The ticket collectors took cover.

The fans set out jauntily on the eight mile hike to Wembley. The English might shut down their underground and their buses, board up their windows and close their pubs, but they wouldn't stop Scotland hammering them at Wembley, no way. Some Scots went by taxi, nine pounds a time. A Rolls Royce was cheered as it flashed by, carrying tartan tammies wolfing fish suppers. Some youngsters made their way through the crowds on roller skates.

When Gary reached Wembley his feet were sore, but he felt better. "Scotland, Scotland," the fans howled outside the ground. "Scotland, Scotland," the insiders responded. If there were any English fans present, they were mute.

Unlike Billy, Gary had no ticket. He knew all he had to do was to slip the gateman a fiver.

"No chance, son," said the man.

"Here's anither fiver."

"No chance, I said. Back you go."

A bobby moved in to pull Gary away. Billy shouted

back, "If ye canny get in, Ah'll see ye here efter the gemme."

The tannoy announced the Scottish team. Each player got a huge roar, especially the goalkeeper. *Kennedy. Jardine, McGrain. Munro. McQueen. Rioch. Dalglish. Conn. Parlane. MacDougall. Duncan.* Immortals all.

Gary moved quickly to another queue. The deafening roars told him the teams had come out. The line moved maddeningly slowly. The excited transistor commentary made Gary feel frantic. This time, he pushed two Scottish five pound notes under the wire mesh.

No luck. He looked desperately along the boundary wall, but the ring of policemen did not look welcoming.

Why Are We So Good? inquired the crowd. All we are Saying is Give us a Goal.

The goal came, Stewart Kennedy statuesque. Gary, ear to the transistor, was sickened. The laughing policemen didn't make him feel any better. Goals two and three. Kennedy's father in tears in the stand.

Gary paced back and forward outside the stadium. "What a Load of Rubbish!" the fans intoned as they straggled out of the ground, long before the end.

Gary waited for his brother. The electronic scoreboard signalled *England 5, Scotland 1. We wish you a safe and pleasant journey home.*

Some of the Scots sang defiantly, trying to keep the pain level manageable. As they trudged along Kensington High Street, a bagpiper played a lament. When will we see your likes again?

"Well," Billy summed up, "Scotland wis fuck'n rubbish. They'll have tae improve afore we come back again next time."

Aye, said Gary to no one. Aye, mebbe.

Homeward, tae think again. It was like a retreat of the

138

wounded from the field of battle. Occasional bleats of "Scotland, Scotland" started, but no one had the heart for it.

Back in the scheme, everything seemed greyer - even Mrs Duffy, as she silently received her boys back. Prince, kicked for his enthusiasm, slunk back into the kitchen.

Gary could hardly wait to get out of the house again, to trudge the streets alone, until dark.

He hated the place. But it was home, wasn't it?

The hating of Ezra

You want to know why I hate Ezra, why I want to spit when I hear his name? Let me tell you. I hate him with all my heart. Oh yes, I know many people admire him and worship the ground he walks on. But I hate him.

Want to know the problem with Ezra? He doesn't know when to stop, that's his problem.

I didn't realise that at first. He didn't strike me as a leader. He studied a great deal as a young man, too much, in fact. He spent his time pouring over the scrolls; but he didn't seem much like a man of action.

Neither was I, then. I was forever composing poems, songs, playing the lyre. My problem was that I liked the tavern too much. And the girls, yes the girls. Ezra didn't have time for such frivolities. Damn him.

I have lived through nightmares, and Ezra has been one of them.

Looking back on it all, Babylon was the best time. In those days, all I knew of Jerusalem was through the stories that my father, and the elders of the community, told me. They had never been to Jerusalem either. They had heard the stories from their grandfathers, who had heard them from their grandfathers. There were tales about the magnificence and wonder of Solomon's great temple. I can recite the dimensions – sixty cubits long, twenty cubits wide, and thirty cubits high! I even made up a little song about it.....

The stories of the elders gave me a yearning to return, even though I'd never been there, if you know what I mean. And the tales about the heroes of the faith made me proud to be a Jew, even though we were a defeated people. I wept every time I heard about the beautiful temple burning as Nebuchadnezzar's troops sacked the city. I uttered cries of vengeance when I heard whispered words about rape, and the dashing of Jewish children's heads against the rocks. I composed sad songs about them, lamentations which were popular when the wine flowed in the taverns.

Do you know this? People like to be melancholy. They weep, they drink, they sing, and then they go home happy-sad. *By the waters of Babylon we sat down and wept, when we remembered Zion.* Sure, but, believe me, we enjoyed drinking from the well of sorrow mixed with wine!

Not Ezra, though. He was born an old man.

No, Babylon wasn't so bad. The Persians were fine, as long as we Jews didn't cause any bother. Some of our people did very well, very well indeed. My father, Asahel, for instance. He became a merchant in Nippur, where we lived, buying and selling things at the markets. He stayed true to the faith of his fathers – we had prayers morning and night - and he instructed me in the stories of the heroes. Yes, my father sat down and wept by the waters of Babylon when he remembered Zion – but when the chance came to go there for the first time in his life, he turned it down quickly. He had heard the reports of how poor things were in Judah.

"Jonathan," he used to say to me, "Yahweh is good to us here."

There were temples wherever you looked – 15 alone in Nippur. When I went to visit Babylon itself, I was overwhelmed. There were more than fifty temples and lots of small shrines. Each street was named after a god. A friendly priest offered to show me the main temple of Marduk. He led me through a whole series of outer courts, then into the inner courts. Finally we came to a room at the centre. Up on the big platform was a gigantic image of Marduk, sitting on a throne made of pure gold. It was so overpowering that I was tempted to fall down in awe. Then I remembered I was a Jew.

It worried me, though. If Yahweh really was the true God, why were His people in exile? Why was Solomon's temple in cinders when Marduk was sitting in all his majestic glory in a golden room? Why were the people who lived in Yahweh's land starving, while Babylon was so rich?

On the journey back home, the questions kept buzzing through my mind, like troublesome flies. I wondered whether Yahweh would strike me down for even thinking about these things.

I determined that when I got back to Nippur, I would find the answers.

I went to see Ezra. (This was before I hated him. Not that I ever particularly liked him, but at that time I did not detest him.) His skin was pale because he spent so much time indoors studying the holy scrolls. Though he was no more than twenty, he exuded mustiness.

For the first time in my life I found myself asking serious questions. Ezra looked at me quietly, but intensely. "You must have faith," he said eventually. "Yahweh will lead you to the truth. But if you are serious, you must dedicate your life to Him. You won't find Him in the taverns, or in your songs. You must give up the way the infidels live. You have a choice to make."

I think he was flattered that I was asking the advice of

a younger man, though his expressionless face showed no glimpse of pride. What should I study? "Torah," he said simply. "Read the Law of Moses night and day. Study Torah, and prostrate yourself before Yahweh."

I did, I did. Of course, I knew the Law of Moses. I had been taught its precepts at home. I had studied the scriptures – in fact, I was the best at Hebrew in the shabbat school. But now I was in earnest. I read and reread the stories of Moses's confrontations with Pharoah, and the tribulations of my people in the wilderness. I studied the laws of Yahweh, delivered on Sinai and spoken through the words of His servants, the prophets. I became obsessed with Torah, with the beautiful moral poetry of Yahweh.

No, I did not give up the taverns, or the songs. Or the women. I was not ready for that yet. The poetry I composed, though, became more serious. The strophes had a harder, less sentimental edge to them.

The questions, unfortunately, did not go away. In fact, they multiplied. The more I studied the Law of Moses, the more questions I had about the purposes of Yahweh. Instead of becoming clearer, He became more mysterious. The closer I got to Him, the further away He moved. What was the point of being a chosen people if all you got was grief and lamentation? Maybe Marduk really was more powerful. I was glad of Ezra's advice, but I needed something more.

It was Shimei who provided it. Some said he was about eighty years old, but no one knew for sure. He lived on his own, and he lived in a world of his own. He had a wild look about him. Now and again a look of ecstasy crossed his face, as if he had moved into heaven itself.

It was Shimei who introduced me to the Prophet. That was all Shimei ever called him. The Prophet. When I went to see the old man and told him about my quest, he

144

smiled as if he had been expecting me. "Blessed be Yahweh for ever!" he exclaimed, before breaking into a strange little dance. I liked him, even though I was slightly in awe of him.

The Prophet, he told me, had died about fifty years ago. He had lived in one of the small communities on the edge of the Euphrates river.

What was he like? Oh, nothing remarkable.

"If you had seen him walking along the road, you would have thought how ordinary he was," said Shimei.

"He never thought that he was anybody special. Even now, only a few people appreciate him."

The Prophet's hero, Shimei explained, was Isaiah. "But I think the Prophet was even greater than Isaiah."

Greater than Isaiah? How could an unexceptional man living in exile by the Euphrates, one who was neither a scribe nor a priest, be greater than the great Isaiah of Jerusalem?

As if reading my thoughts, Shimei began speaking in flawless Hebrew, rocking back and forward as he spoke.

Comfort, comfort my people,
says your God.
Speak tenderly to Jerusalem,
and cry to her
that her warfare is ended,
that her iniquity is pardoned,
that she has received from Yahweh's hand
double for all her sins.

Shimei recited the words like a man in a trance. He was caught up. I could hardly believe what I was hearing. The poetry! Shimei went on.

Have you not known? Have you not heard?

145

Has it not been told you from the beginning?
Have you not understood from the foundations of the
  earth?
It is he who sits above the circle of the earth,
and its inhabitants are like grasshoppers;
who stretches out the heavens like a curtain,
and spreads them like a tent to dwell in;
who brings princes to nought,
and who makes the rulers of the earth as nothing.
Have you not known, have you not heard?
Yahweh is the everlasting God,
the Creator of the ends of the earth.

The words of the Prophet burned in my brain. The
poetry scalded me, the majesty of the theology
overwhelmed me. I was intoxicated by divine words. In
that little house in Nippur, I was not so much seeking as
being sought, not so much questioning as being questioned,
addressed, loved.

For the first time in my life I understood with my
heart: and in the excitement, I passed out completely.

The words of the Prophet consumed me, and Shimei
became my teacher. All I knew was that I agreed with
Shimei's judgment: Isaiah's shy pupil was even greater than
his master. Shimei recited the works of the Prophet for me,
and let me read some scrolls with his words beautifully
inscribed upon them. I pored over them, hungry for
spiritual enlightenment and experience.

What excited me was that the Prophet understood
Yahweh not as a little tribal god, but as the creator of the
whole universe! Yet, He was gentle, too. *Comfort, comfort
my people, says your God. Speak tenderly to Jerusalem....*

As a poet myself, I loved the exquisite words which
rolled off my tongue as I read from the scrolls. Shimei and
I would take turns to read them aloud. Over the next few
months, I memorised the texts. They told me things I

needed to hear.

What did it mean to be chosen? It meant being a servant for the sake of the whole world, said the Prophet. Not only that, Yahweh would bring back the scattered people of Israel to Jerusalem.

> *How beautiful upon the mountains*
> *are the feet of him who brings good tidings,*
> *who publishes peace, who brings tidings of good,*
> *who publishes salvation,*
> *who says to Zion, "Your God reigns."*
> *Hark, your watchmen lift up their voice,*
> *together they sing for joy;*
> *for eye to eye they see*
> *the return of the Lord to Zion.*
> *Break forth together into singing,*
> *you waste places of Jerusalem.*

There was only one thing for it. I must go to Jerusalem.

My mother wept. My father understood. Part of him wanted to come with me – but only a small part. He gave me his blessing.

Of course, there had been several official expeditions before I left Babylon. Sheshbazzar had led the first lot. I had heard the tales of the difficulties they encountered in Jerusalem. The pilgrims had been deeply affected by the poverty of Judah, and the religious apathy. Once they had settled, they laid the foundations of a new temple in the city of David. It had been a long, hard struggle, but they eventually managed to finish the building. When the temple was dedicated, many people wept – not with joy, but with sadness – when they compared the new building with the splendour of Solomon's temple.

I found the journey tiring and difficult. My three travelling companions and I endured terrible heat. We

147

were robbed by brigands. I kept my spirits alive by reciting
the words of the Prophet.

They who wait on for Yahweh
shall renew their strength,
they shall mount up with wings like eagles,
they shall run and not be weary,
they shall walk and not faint.

When we reached Jerusalem, the first thing I did was
to go to the temple. At first sight of the modest building,
my mind travelled back to Babylon and the splendour of
the temple of Marduk. Nevertheless, this was the house of
Yahweh, and this was the holy city.

My faith would be tested in this holy city, especially by
Ezra. Oh, how I hate that man! But I am running ahead of
myself.

It was in the city of David that I first met Miriam. The
fact that she was a Samaritan did not trouble me. The
Samaritans were part of our history: they worshipped
Yahweh and they kept the Law of Moses. Some of our
leaders rejected them, saying that they had been corrupted
by intermarriage with foreigners. Miriam told me that
when the Samaritans offered to help with the rebuilding of
the temple in Jerusalem, the offer was thrown back in their
faces.

How can I tell you about Miriam? Of all the beautiful
women I have ever seen – and I have seen quite a few –
she was the most beautiful. The fact that she loved Yahweh
so purely added to her attraction. An unmarried man and
woman were not supposed to be alone together, but we
easily found ways of meeting. I introduced her to the
Prophet, and she was entranced.

Miriam captivated me, entirely. Night and day I

thought about her. She set my heart singing, and I could not stop writing poetry and songs about her. I adapted and re-wrote some of the love songs I had heard in the taverns of Nippur.

How fair and pleasant you are,
O loved one, delectable maiden!
You are stately as a palm tree,
and your breasts are like its clusters.
Oh, may your breasts be like clusters of the vine,
and the scent of your breath like apples,
and your kisses like the best wine
that goes down smoothly,
gliding over lips and teeth.

I was drunk with love. I was exultant, delirious, ecstatic.

We married in Samaria in the Spring.

You have ravished my heart, my sister, my bride,
you have ravished my heart with a glance of your eyes,
with one jewel of your necklace.

How sweet is your love, my sister, my bride!

We made our home in Jerusalem, where I was given work as a temple musician. My happiness was complete when our twin children, Asahel and Shimei were born. To think that if I had stayed in Babylon I would have missed all this! Yahweh is good!

But not all of his servants are. Especially Ezra. Yes, especially him.

At first I was pleased when I heard that Nehemiah, the eunuch, son of Halcaliah, was coming to Jerusalem. From what I knew of him he was a good organiser, and not a fanatic. He was the cupbearer of King Artaxerxes at the palace in Susa. I remember him coming with the king to his winter gardens in Babylon. Nehemiah served the king well, while remaining a Jew loyal to the faith of his fathers. The first thing he did was to rebuild the walls of Jerusalem. He was very brave. Some of the Samaritans gave him trouble, but he stuck to his task.

The day on which the walls of the city were dedicated was a special one. It was the twenty-fifth day of the month of Elul, and the sun was high in the sky. The ceremony began at the Sheep Gate. I was in charge of the choir, and I must say, with pride, that they sang magnificently. After the prayers of the priests, the ceremony ended with temple sacrifices.

I admired what Nehemiah had achieved. Towards the end of his second term as governor, though, I became alarmed by his outbursts against foreigners. Then, one day at the temple, he took me aside. "I need more help in organising this community," he said. "We need more scribes who understand Torah. We need priests who are truly dedicated to Yahweh. I have written to the King Artaxerxes to send me a priest from Babylon to take charge of this."

The man's name, he said, was Ezra, son of Seraiah.

I watched him arrive. He brought with him priests, Levites, scribes, temple musicians and workmen. He also brought gold and silver offerings, and utensils for the temple of Yahweh.

I recognised him immediately, even though he had aged considerably. The face was still pale, the eyes intense. I stayed in the shadows.

Ezra got to work quickly. He weighed and measured and recorded all the gifts with great meticulousness. All those who had returned from exile brought offerings to the altar to be burned as sacrifices to Yahweh. They offered 12 bulls, 96 rams and 77 lambs; they also offered 12 goats to purify themselves from sin. Ezra entered it all in his book.

An assembly of all the people, men, women and children was called. They gathered at dawn in the square just inside the Water Gate, and sat in rows on the ground. A big wooden platform had been erected. Ezra's men stood at either side of the platform.

I watched Ezra mount the stage. As he stood high above the people, a flicker of pride crossed his face. He looked like a man whose hour had come.

The seated people looked up at the priest. For a moment, time seemed to stand still in the square. The silence was broken as Ezra unrolled the scroll in his hand - the Law of Moses. At this, the people stood up as one man. Ezra cried, "Praise Yahweh, the great God!" The people raised their arms in the air and shouted, "Amen! Amen!" then they knelt in worship, their faces to the ground.

From dawn till noon, Ezra read the Law of Moses to the people. His Levites translated the Hebrew into Aramaic, so that the people could understand it all. They listened attentively. You could tell how much Ezra loved the words by the way he read the sacred texts. Even the purification regulations were read out as if they were the best news anyone could ever wish to hear.

The impact was overwhelming. When Ezra eventually finished, the square was filled with the sound of weeping. The people were convicted by the demands of Yahweh, as delivered by His servant Ezra.

He dismissed the crowd. "Do not be sad on this holy day," he told them. "Go home and have a feast. Share your bread and wine with those who don't have enough." There was something good about the man. And yet, he left me feeling very apprehensive. I knew that a day of reckoning would come soon.

It is raining very hard in the temple square. All the men of Judah and Benjamin have been summoned to an assembly. The word has gone out: any who fail to come will have their property confiscated, and will be ejected from the community. The people are trembling.

Ezra is once again high above the crowd. Every eye is fixed on his slightly stooped figure. There is tension in the air.

Ezra starts to speak. He is addressing Yahweh.

"Lord God, I am too ashamed to raise my head in your presence. Our sins pile up, high above our heads; they reach as high as the heavens. From the days of our ancestors until now, we, your people, have sinned greatly. Because of this, we were carried away as prisoners.

"Now, for a short time, O Yahweh, you have been gracious to us and have let some of us escape from slavery and live in safety in this holy place. Now, we have again disobeyed your commands. We have filled the land from end to end with disgusting, filthy actions. Your people have intermarried with foreigners, wicked people. Do not destroy us in your righteous anger, we ask."

The heavens are weeping. Ezra is weeping. The tension is unbearable. He speaks to the crowd directly.

"You have brought guilt on Israel by marrying foreign women. Israel has become corrupted. Now then, confess your sins to Yahweh, the God of your ancestors. Separate yourselves from the foreigners living in our land and get rid of your foreign wives."

The people stand up and shout, "We will do whatever you say."

At this moment, I am consumed by a burning hatred for this pale-faced fanatic. I am being asked to choose between my faith as a Jew, and my wife, who has brought me the unspeakable joy of human love. He is commanding me to divorce Miriam and send her away, or face exclusion from the community of Yahweh for ever.

I know that there are people in that crowd who do not agree with Ezra, but they are afraid. Afraid of Ezra. Afraid of Yahweh's wrath.

I must speak. I stand up. I am trembling.

"Ezra, son of Seraiah," I cry, falteringly. The crowd, seated, look round at me, anxiously. Ezra fixes me with a baleful stare. He wears the look of a man who does not like to be challenged, a man who knows that Yahweh is on his side.

"Ezra, son of Seraiah," I stammered again, "you are mistaken."

You can actually hear the people hold their breath.

"I cannot speak for the others here. I can only testify myself. My wife, Miriam, loves Yahweh. She loves the Law of Moses. We have made sacred promises to each other, in Yahweh's name, that we will live together for the rest of our lives. Are you telling me that the purposes of Yahweh are served by breaking vows made to him?"

Ezra is staring at me. At first, he looks as if he cannot speak, then he says, "Jonathan, son of Asahel, how dare you challenge the will of Yahweh, the Holy One of Israel! Years ago, in Babylon, I faced you with a choice. It seems that you were not strong enough to walk in the way of Yahweh. Your wife is a Samaritan woman, and the Samaritans are our enemies. Once you have divorced your wife, you will need a period of penitence before you can be restored to the community. You will never again play your lyre in the temple of Yahweh."

Ezra's men lead the cries of "Amen!" and the crowd gradually join in the chants. Ezra makes to turn away.

"Ezra, son of Seraiah," I cry again. I am furious. I am beyond fear for my own safety. The crowd quietens. "Ezra, you are an evil man."

His cheeks show colour for the first time. I am shouting. I cannot help it.

"You think that Yahweh's chief concern is for the racial purity of Israel and for correct religious observance. But Yahweh looks on the inward heart. Those who love

154

Yahweh are those who do His will. There are many sons of Abraham who can recite Torah but whose hearts are hard as stone."

Then, I go too far.

"Ezra, there are foreign prostitutes who have a more generous love for the poor and the outcast than you do. Maybe Yahweh prefers them to you."

I already know that I am a man in exile again. Miriam and Asahel and Shimei and I will walk, hand in hand, beyond these walls, with tears streaming down our faces. I know that I will never again worship Yahweh in the temple I love.

Yes, I will face the terrible pain of exclusion from the community of faith.

I have made my choice.

How quickly the time goes by! Asahel and Shimei are now fourteen years old. They miss their mother terribly, as, of course, I do. Not a day goes by when I do not think of her, long for her. I console myself by writing more poems and songs about Miriam. This is a painful exercise, but it helps me.

I am still depressed by it all. Ezra, of course, has won. The temple is working very efficiently, and the priests are in charge of the community. Racial purity is maintained. If people are found to have any past "corruptions" in their family history, they are dismissed. People spy on each other, and report any breaches of the law. Everything is recorded in Ezra's book. All this matters more than love for Yahweh. That, to my way of thinking, is the true corruption.

But I have lost the argument.

There is something I want to tell you, my friends. It is almost too painful to narrate.

When the disease carried Miriam away, I received a message from Ezra. He sent it to Samaria by way of one of his spies. Here is what he said: "The death of your Samaritan wife is Yahweh's judgment upon you for your infidelity to his Law. But now I want to present you with a new choice. If you repent and come back to Jerusalem, and if you show that you have not been contaminated by Samaritan ways, I will allow you to rejoin the community of Israel."

You know something? With this offer, Ezra thought he was being compassionate. Truly. I both hate him and pity him.

I think a lot about Ezra, trying to understand him. When I'm feeling generous, I see him as a good man corrupted. He has always wanted the best for Yahweh, for Israel. I even respect his achievements.

What is the problem with Ezra? Let me try again. The real problem with Ezra is that his cold-eyed goodness moves too easily into cruelty. When I think about it, I have never seen him smile.

The man has no imagination, no class, no heart.

I suppose I deal with my grief by writing. Apart from the poems and songs, I am working on a story. It's about a village prophet, who is called by Yahweh to preach the mercy and forgiveness of God in Assyria. He doesn't want to do it because he hates foreigners and he thinks God should hate foreigners, too. So he runs away to sea and gets swallowed up by a big fish. The fish vomits him back on dry land, and Yahweh is waiting for him. He has to go to Nineveh!

I'm writing a piece of history as well. It's a true story about a Hebrew man called Elimech. In the time when the Judges ruled Israel, he went with his wife, Naomi, and their two sons from his home in Bethlehem to Moab because

156

there was a great famine in Judah. One of his sons married a Moabite woman, Ruth. When both her husband and his father died, Ruth chose not to stay in Moab but to go to Judah with her mother in law. It was a very brave decision. In Bethlehem, Ruth met a Hebrew widower, Boaz, and they got married. Through their marriage, this Moabite woman became the great grandmother of King David.

I don't think Ezra would like these stories. That zealot would have refused King David citizenship in Israel because he had foreign blood in his family! And he wanted me to give up Miriam, who is no different from Ruth, great grandmother of Israel's greatest king! That's why I hate the bastard.

These pieces of mine aren't exactly sacred scripture. I am writing them for my children's sake, to tell them that Yahweh is bigger and more generous than we think. Certainly more generous than Ezra thinks.

Oh, how I miss the temple in Jerusalem! I worship sometimes at the temple in Gerizim, but it's not the same. Most of all, of course, I miss Miriam. She brought me life. Part of Ezra's trouble is that he has never known the love of a good woman.

When I hear about what is happening in Jerusalem, I grieve. But when I look at Asahel and Shimei, I dream. I dream of a servant Israel, bringing Yahweh's love and mercy to all the world.

Despite Ezra, I will live and die a Jew, loyal to the faith of my fathers. I am writing this document to let you know, after my death, why things happened the way they did: and also to keep alive the Prophet's hope of a new thing.

Every valley shall be lifted up,
and every mountain and hill be made low.
And the glory of the Lord shall be revealed,

and all flesh shall see it together,
for the mouth of the Lord has spoken.

Yes, yes. On my better days, I can say that God is good. On black days, which are many, I see in my mind a pale, tense face.

Ezra son of Seraiah, may you find forgiveness – from Yahweh, but not from me.